The Ultimate Quiz Book

General knowledge

The Ultimate Quiz Book

General knowledge

Cosmo Brown

Bath · New York · Singapore · Hong Kong · Cologne · Delhi
Melbourne · Amsterdam · Johannesburg · Auckland · Shenzhen

This edition published by Parragon in 2011

Parragon
Queen Street House
4 Queen Street
Bath BA1 1HE, UK

Designed & produced by Design Principals, Warminster

Front cover image: Photo by Neil A. Armstrong/NASA/
Time Life Pictures/ © Getty Images

ISBN: 978-1-4454-2816-1

Printed in China

CONTENTS

ART & LITERATURE
QUESTIONS 1-23

CINEMA & TELEVISION
QUESTIONS 24-45

GEOGRAPHY
QUESTIONS 46-65

HISTORY
QUESTIONS 66-87

MUSIC
QUESTIONS 88-109

PEOPLE
QUESTIONS 110-131

SCIENCE & NATURE
QUESTIONS 132-153

SPORTS & GAMES
QUESTIONS 154-176

GENERAL KNOWLEDGE
QUESTIONS 177-200

ART & LITERATURE
WORDS AND PICTURES (1)

1

Which Brontë sister wrote the novel *Jane Eyre*?

2

Who painted the ceiling of the Sistine Chapel?

3

Who commanded the *Nautilus* in Jules Verne's classic tale?

4

Which British sculptor is noted for using natural materials?

5

With which novel did Aravind Adiga win the 2008 Booker Prize?

6

What was writer Joseph Conrad's first language?

7

Which museum is home to the *Mona Lisa*?

8

Name the third part of the *Lord of the Rings* trilogy.

9

Who is the creator of Discworld?

10

What do the initials stand for in J K Rowling?

11

What was the first James Bond book?

12

In which century did Rococo art and architecture develop?

ART & LITERATURE
CHILDREN'S BOOKS

1

Name the dog in the Famous Five books.

2

Who first illustrated *Alice's Adventures in Wonderland*?

3

Who is the hero of the novel *Lorna Doone*?

4

Which is the third book in the *Harry Potter* series?

5

Who wrote "How the Leopard Got His Spots"?

6

In *Peter Pan*, what are the names of Wendy's brothers?

7

What does "BFG" stand for in Roald Dahl's story?

8

Who wrote *The Wonderful Wizard of Oz*?

9

Who does Charlotte save in *Charlotte's Web*?

10

Name the rabbit trio in *The Tales of Peter Rabbit*.

11

What children's classic was written by Antoine de Saint-Exupéry?

12

What are the Grimm Brothers' first names?

ART & LITERATURE
MODERN ART

1

Who was the best-known exponent of Action Painting?

2

Which artistic movement began in Paris in 1907?

3

Which bombed Spanish town inspired a Picasso painting?

4

Who turned a can of soup into a work of art?

5

Who created the Beatles' "Sgt Pepper" album cover?

6

What is the image in Jasper Johns' painting *Flag*?

7

Which American artist painted *Nighthawks*?

8

Who is the artist brother of Clement Freud?

9

Which Australian artist painted a series of Ned Kelly pictures?

10

In which country was Francis Bacon born?

11

Which English artist is famous for Op Art?

12

Which artist was expelled from the Surrealist movement in 1939?

ART & LITERATURE
POETS AND POETRY

1

Where is Poets' Corner?

2

Who wrote "The Rime of the Ancient Mariner"?

3

Who became Poet Laureate in 2009?

4

What was lost and regained in the poems of John Milton?

5

How many lines has a clerihew?

6

Which poet's birthday is celebrated on 25 January?

7

What do the initials in W H Auden stand for?

8

Which American poet's only novel was entitled *The Bell Jar*?

9

To which bird did John Keats compose an ode?

10

Which poet was dean of St Paul's Cathedral?

11

What was Percy Shelley's middle name?

12

Which poet was knighted in 1969?

ART & LITERATURE
FAMOUS PEN NAMES

1

How is Charles Lutwidge Dodgson better known?

2

Which best-selling author is David Cornwell?

3

What was Samuel Langhorne Clemens' more famous name?

4

Which British female author is really Franklin Birkinshaw?

5

Which 18th-century French writer was François Marie Arouet?

6

Mary Westmacott is a pen name of which famous author?

7

William Sydney Porter wrote short stories under which name?

8

What was the pen name of Eric Blair?

9

Mary Ann Evans is the real name of which English novelist?

10

What was the pen name of Baroness Karen Blixen?

11

Under what name did Emily Brontë first publish *Wuthering Heights*?

12

Frederic Dannay and Manfred B Lee are which US mystery writer?

ART & LITERATURE
WORDS AND PICTURES (2)

1

Who wrote *Of Mice and Men*?

2

Which French artist was born in the Virgin Islands?

3

What did the crocodile swallow in *Peter Pan*?

4

Whose portrait of Winston Churchill upset the sitter?

5

Who wrote the novel *Jurassic Park*?

6

Which artist's Pink Period followed his Blue Period?

7

What poem begins: "I wandered lonely as a cloud"?

8

Who is *The Hobbit* referred to in the title?

9

Who wrote *The Hitchhiker's Guide to the Galaxy*?

10

What was the artist Raphael's real name?

11

New Grub Street was a novel by which English author?

12

The Kiss is a famous sculpture by which artist?

ART & LITERATURE
THE WORLD OF CHARLES DICKENS

1

In which town was Charles Dickens born?

2

Which Dickens novel was unfinished at his death?

3

Uriah Heep is a character in which novel?

4

What is the Artful Dodger's real name?

5

With which actress did Charles Dickens have an affair?

6

What are the two cities in *A Tale of Two Cities*?

7

Which Dickens character lent her name to an umbrella?

8

In which novel is Thomas Gradgrind a character?

9

Name Scrooge's deceased partner in *A Christmas Carol*.

10

Where was Little Dorrit born?

11

Who was the headmaster of Dotheboys Hall?

12

Which Dickens novel revolves around the Gordon Riots?

ART & LITERATURE
WHO PAINTED THESE?

....

1

The Blue Boy

....

2

Girl with a Pearl Earring

....

3

The Hay Wain

....

4

Children's Games

....

5

The Kiss

....

6

The Last Supper

....

7

The Scream

....

8

The Raft of the Medusa

....

9

The Laughing Cavalier

....

10

The Starry Night

....

11

The Garden of Earthly Delights

....

12

The Monarch of the Glen

....

ART & LITERATURE
CLASSIC CHARACTERS

1

Name the Three Musketeers.

2

Who is the Mayor of Casterbridge?

3

Which American classic begins: "Call me Ishmael"?

4

What was Madame Bovary's first name?

5

In which Jane Austen novel does Colonel Brandon feature?

6

Who lived at 221b Baker Street?

7

Who is the heroine of William Thackeray's *Vanity Fair*?

8

What is the name of Don Quixote's horse?

9

In which Russian novel is Raskolnikov the central character?

10

In *Gulliver's Travels*, what is Gulliver's first name?

11

Who is the cricket-loving gentleman thief?

12

Who was the last of the Mohicans?

ART & LITERATURE
LITERARY SLEUTHS

1

Who created the aristocratic detective Lord Peter Wimsey?

2

In which novel does private eye Philip Marlowe first appear?

3

Inspector Lestrade is constantly outdone by which super sleuth?

4

Who is the teenage detective of River Heights?

5

Who solves the mystery of *The Murders of the Rue Morgue*?

6

Which priestly detective goes about with an umbrella?

7

Which hard-boiled US private eye calls his gun "Betsy"?

8

In which country does Inspector Napoleon Bonaparte pursue crime?

9

What is Inspector Maigret's first name?

10

Which US crime writer worked for the Pinkerton Detective Agency?

11

Who is the author of the Inspector Alleyn books?

12

What is the name of the enquiring monk in *The Name of the Rose*?

ART & LITERATURE
WORDS AND PICTURES (3)

1

What is France's top literary prize?

2

Where is the Prado museum?

3

What nationality is the writer Margaret Atwood?

4

Who wrote twelve volumes about Casanova?

5

In whose novels is Richard Hannay the hero?

6

Who sometimes wrote under the pseudonym "Parson Lot"?

7

What do sculptors make as a preliminary model?

8

Which American poet was charged with treason in 1945?

9

What is the term for a wall painting?

10

What was Jane Austen's first published novel?

11

Whose first of many books was called *Jigsaw*?

12

Which artist/naturalist illustrated *The Birds of America*?

ART & LITERATURE
NUMBERS GAME

1

Who wrote *One Flew Over the Cuckoo's Nest*?

2

Who wrote *A Kid for Two Farthings*?

3

Who wrote *Three Men in a Boat*?

4

Who wrote *The Fourth Protocol*?

5

Who wrote *Five Children and It*?

6

Who wrote *Now We Are Six*?

7

Who wrote *Seven Pillars of Wisdom*?

8

Who wrote *When Eight Bells Toll*?

9

Who wrote *Up On Cloud Nine*?

10

Who wrote *Ten Little Indians*?

11

Who wrote *Eleven Days*?

12

Who wrote *Twelfth Night*?

ART & LITERATURE
ARTISTS IN THE FRAME

1

Who was the first president of the Royal Academy?

2

Which Italian artist's name means "little barrel"?

3

Who turned his garden at Giverny into an artistic endeavour?

4

Which French painter lived and worked in Tahiti?

5

In which country was Marc Chagall born?

6

Which 17th-century Italian artist was wanted for murder?

7

Who was the first English artist to be made a Dame?

8

What do the initials stand for in L S Lowry?

9

What was English artist George Stubbs' favourite model?

10

Which Flemish painter was knighted by Charles I?

11

What name was Domenikos Theotocopoulos known by?

12

Which US artist wrote *The Gentle Art of Making Enemies*?

. . . .

1

Who was William Shakespeare's wife?

. . . .

2

Who is warned: "Beware the ides of March"?

. . . .

3

On which Shakespeare play is the musical *Kiss Me Kate* based?

. . . .

4

What war is the background to *Troilus and Cressida*?

. . . .

5

In which play is Leontes king of Sicily?

. . . .

6

Who are the rival families in *Romeo and Juliet*?

. . . .

7

Which play is set in one place and takes place all in one day?

. . . .

8

Which play has "Athens" in the title?

. . . .

9

Shakespeare's birthday is on which saint's day?

. . . .

10

In which forest is *As You Like It* set?

. . . .

11

What are the names of King Lear's three daughters?

. . . .

12

Complete the title of Shakespeare's poem: "The Rape of . . . ".

. . . .

ART & LITERATURE
WORDS AND PICTURES (4)

1

Whose first novel was *High Fidelity*?

2

Who sculpted the lions in London's Trafalgar Square?

3

Which pier features in a George Orwell book title?

4

How many parts to a triptych?

5

Which revolutionary arts movement was founded in 1916?

6

Which Alexandre Dumas was the novelist – father or son?

7

Which French sculptor created The Statue of Liberty?

8

Name the five Bennet girls in *Pride and Prejudice*.

9

What is Lascaux in France famous for?

10

Who is the captain of the *Pequod* in *Moby Dick*?

11

Which Flemish artist became court painter to Charles I?

12

Which Russian writer died at a railway station?

ART & LITERATURE
MORE POETS AND POETRY

1

Who wrote "Hiawatha"?

2

Who was Poet Laureate from 1930 to 1967?

3

What do the initials stand for in T S Eliot?

4

How many lines in a sonnet?

5

Which poet is a former member of The Scaffold pop group?

6

Whose translation of *Beowulf* was published in 2000?

7

Who composed a sonnet "Upon Westminster Bridge"?

8

Which W H Auden poem was read in *Four Weddings and a Funeral*?

9

Which English poet committed suicide at the age of 17?

10

What was Lord Byron's first name?

11

Which poet did Spanish Nationalists murder in 1936?

12

Who started off with *Making Cocoa for Kingsley Amis*?

ART & LITERATURE
PLAYS AND PLAYWRIGHTS

1

Which playwright won the Nobel Prize for Literature in 2005?

2

The Cocktail Party and *The Family Reunion* are by whom?

3

Whose first dramatic success was a *Five Finger Exercise*?

4

On which play is the musical *My Fair Lady* based?

5

In which play is Blanche DuBois a key character?

6

Who wrote the Oedipus trilogy?

7

In which country was Tom Stoppard born?

8

Which playwright was stabbed to death in Deptford in 1593?

9

Which "Monologues" are all about women?

10

Who wrote *Caesar and Cleopatra*?

11

Which Arthur Miller play has witchcraft as its theme?

12

Which playwright was a former member of the IRA?

ART & LITERATURE
OLD MASTERS

1

With which city is Canaletto most famously associated?

2

Who painted *The Naked Maja*?

3

Which French Impressionist painted *Westminster Bridge* in 1871?

4

William Hogarth's *A Rake's Progress* comprises how many paintings?

5

Which Titian masterpiece was saved for the nation in 2009?

6

La Goulue was which French artist's most celebrated model?

7

Who painted the execution of Emperor Maximilian of Mexico?

8

Whose portrait of Henry VIII defined the king's image?

9

The Dancing Class is the work of which French artist?

10

Which Pre-Raphaelite artist painted *Ophelia*?

11

Which English artist's first names are Joseph Mallord William?

12

Who was the foremost artist of the French Revolution?

1

What fantasy kingdom is just through the wardrobe?

2

Whose novels are set in Wessex?

3

In which English classic will you find Brobdingnag?

4

What has London become in George Orwell's *1984*?

5

Who is the Shire home to?

6

Which US writer created Yoknapatawpha County?

7

Who is Neverland's most famous resident?

8

Who is the author of the Barsetshire novels?

9

In whose stories does the town of Lake Wobegon feature?

10

In which 1930s classic can Shangri-La be found?

11

What is the name of Professor Challenger's lost world?

12

Llaregyb is an imaginary Welsh town in which famous play?

ART & LITERATURE
20TH-CENTURY CLASSICS

1

Who wrote *Watership Down*?

2

What begins: "Last night I dreamt I went to Manderley again"?

3

Who was Lady Chatterley's lover?

4

The Tin Drum is by which German author?

5

Who is the narrator in the novel *Lolita*?

6

Which Evelyn Waugh novel is a satire on Fleet Street?

7

Napoleon and Snowball are characters in which political novel?

8

Who is the author of the *Raj Quartet*?

9

Holden Caulfield is the hero of which American novel?

10

Which Ernest Hemingway novel is set in the Spanish Civil War?

11

What controversial novel about teenage violence appeared in 1962?

12

Whose only published novel is *To Kill a Mockingbird*?

ART & LITERATURE
MORE MODERN ART

1

Whose art features animals preserved in formaldehyde?

2

Who created the "Angel of the North"?

3

In which year did London's Tate Modern open?

4

Which US artist is best known for his "colour field" painting?

5

Whose artistically unmade bed was a sensation in 1999?

6

Which ex-ad man is a leading patron of contemporary art?

7

What nationality was the Surrealist painter René Magritte?

8

Whose anti-war work, *State Britain*, won the 2007 Turner Prize?

9

American artist Georgia O'Keeffe famously painted what?

10

Henry Moore and David Hockney are both natives of which county?

11

Whaam! is a work by which US Pop Artist?

12

How are Gilbert Proesch and George Passmore better known?

1

Who swims in a pool of her own tears?

2

Who wrote *The Iron Man*?

3

What animal is Baloo in *The Jungle Book*?

4

Name the Amazons in *Swallows and Amazons*.

5

What is "It" in *Five Children and It*?

6

Who was the blind man in *Treasure Island*?

7

Which Anne Fine novel became the film *Mrs Doubtfire*?

8

Who wrote *The Children of the New Forest*?

9

Which Roald Dahl character was named after a foot complaint?

10

In *The Water Babies*, what is Tom's job?

11

Which fictional doctor lived in Puddleby-on-Marsh?

12

What is the final book in the "His Dark Materials" trilogy?

. . . .

1

Who wrote *The Turn of the Screw*?

. . . .

2

Which Cornish village is synonymous with contemporary art?

. . . .

3

In which country was J R R Tolkien born?

. . . .

4

Who is the author of the Waverley novels?

. . . .

5

Which graffiti artist took his work indoors at Bristol in 2009?

. . . .

6

What was the novelist Henry Fielding's "day job"?

. . . .

7

Whose Midlands novels are set in the "Five Towns"?

. . . .

8

Where in Spain is there a Guggenheim Museum?

. . . .

9

Which was the first novel published by Stephen King?

. . . .

10

Who conducted the Owl and the Pussycat's wedding?

. . . .

11

Which 20th-century novelist was a lepidopterist?

. . . .

12

Which Australian artist painted a portrait of the Queen in 2005?

. . . .

1

... Angry Men

2

... Days of the Condor

3

Butterfield ...

4

... Rode Together

5

... Rue Madeleine

6

... Paces to Baker Street

7

... Days to Noon

8

... and a Half Weeks

9

... in the Shade

10

... Degrees of Separation

11

The ... Pennies

12

... Years in Sing Sing

1

What Home Guard platoon does Captain Mainwaring command?

2

In *Frasier*, what is the name of Frasier's first wife?

3

What is the name of the prison in *Porridge*?

4

In *As Time Goes By*, what is Jean's agency called?

5

What are the respective professions of Norm and Cliff in *Cheers*?

6

What is the Vicar of Dibley's church?

7

Rodney Trotter has GCSEs in which two subjects?

8

Name the two elderly female residents in *Fawlty Towers*.

9

Till Death Us Do Part became what in the USA?

10

What are the surnames of Bob and Terry in *The Likely Lads*?

11

What is the UK's longest-running sitcom?

12

What was the name of the senior Yellowcoat in *Hi-de-Hi*?

CINEMA & TELEVISION
WHAT ARE THEIR SCREEN NAMES?

1

Roy Scherer

2

John Charles Carter

3

Margarita Carmen Cansino

4

William Henry Pratt

5

Caryn Elaine Johnson

6

Issur Danielovich

7

Betty Perske

8

Alphonso Joseph d'Abruzzo

9

Krishna Bhanji

10

Diana Fluck

11

Cherilyn Sarkisian

12

Spangler Arlington Brugh

CINEMA & TELEVISION
WESTERN MOVIES

1

Who plays Doc Holliday in *Gunfight at the OK Corral*?

2

In which Western is Gregory Peck a man of the sea?

3

Who directed *The Wild Bunch*?

4

In which film is John Wayne The Ringo Kid?

5

Who are the musical duo in *Cat Ballou*?

6

Who starred in *The Man from Laramie*?

7

Brokeback Mountain is based on whose short story?

8

Ride the High Country is known by which other name?

9

Who plays Vin in *The Magnificent Seven*?

10

Who does Henry Fonda play in *My Darling Clementine*?

11

Who is the female attraction in *Once Upon a Time in the West*?

12

Who directed himself in *One Eyed Jacks*?

CINEMA & TELEVISION
MULTISCREEN (1)

1

Who was TV's first Dr Who?

2

What are the robots in *Blade Runner* called?

3

In which film did Meryl Streep make her big screen debut?

4

On which day of the year did Dean Martin die?

5

Who were the first presenters of BBC's *Crimewatch*?

6

Which film ends with the line: "Nobody's perfect"?

7

Who plays Hawkeye Pierce in the film version of *M.A.S.H*?

8

Which sitcom character has a cat called Vienna?

9

What was James Dean's middle name?

10

Who played Reggie Perrin second time around?

11

Who was first choice for the title role in *Shakespeare in Love*?

12

In which film did Eminem make his movie debut?

CINEMA & TELEVISION
TV CRIMEBUSTERS

1

Who heads the Cold Case Unit in *Waking the Dead*?

2

Who's in charge of Gerry, Jack and Brian?

3

Which New York cop had a penchant for lollipops?

4

In what village does Miss Marple live?

5

Who played the original Starsky and Hutch?

6

Which series spun off from *Z Cars*?

7

Who does Bergerac work for?

8

In which US series was Steve McGarrett a character?

9

Who did Jimmy Smits replace in *NYPD Blue*?

10

What is the name of Superintendent Foyle's driver?

11

Can you name Cracker's long-suffering wife?

12

Who does Philip Glenister play in *Life on Mars*?

CINEMA & TELEVISION
FESTIVALS AND AWARDS

1

What do the initials BAFTA stand for?

2

In which year were the Oscars first presented?

3

Which John Wayne film won him his only Oscar?

4

Who was the first black American actress to win an Oscar?

5

What is the major prize at the Venice Film Festival?

6

Who won both a BAFTA and an Oscar for "Best Actor" in 2008?

7

Who refused his Oscar for "Best Actor" in 1970?

8

Where in Spain is there a major annual film festival?

9

For which film did Jack Nicholson receive his second Oscar?

10

Who was the first Englishman to win an Oscar?

11

Who founded the Sundance Film Festival?

12

Which British film won nine Oscars in 1997?

. . . .

1

Who plays the title role in *Klute*?

. . . .

2

Who directed *American Gangster*?

. . . .

3

What film paired Robert de Niro and Al Pacino for the first time?

. . . .

4

In what film is a cop played by Andy Garcia decapitated?

. . . .

5

Who loses her head in *Seven*?

. . . .

6

Who plays the bounty hunter in *No Country for Old Men*?

. . . .

7

In which film does Albert Finney play an aspiring private eye?

. . . .

8

Which Great Train Robber did Phil Collins play?

. . . .

9

To what does private eye Micky Rourke descend to in *Angel Heart*?

. . . .

10

In which film is Elliott Gould private eye Philip Marlowe?

. . . .

11

Name the private detective played by Jack Nicholson in *Chinatown*.

. . . .

12

In which film did Tony Curtis play Albert DeSalvo?

. . . .

1

Name the resort in the BBC soap *Eldorado*.

2

What killed off Butch Dingle in *Emmerdale*?

3

In which year was *Neighbours* first screened in the UK?

4

Which UK soap made a comeback after 13 years?

5

Actor Ralph Meagher is a familiar face in which soap?

6

Which two real celebrities opened Grants Restaurant in *Brookside*?

7

Which former *EastEnders* star died in 2007?

8

Who played Zubin Khan in *Holby City*?

9

In which British soap did Alvin Stardust play a pub landlord?

10

Which *Casualty* actor's wife and son have also been in the show?

11

Who is soap actress Suzanne Packer's famous brother?

12

Billy Crystal was the gay son of the Campbells in which US soap?

CINEMA & TELEVISION
MULTISCREEN (2)

1

In which city is the TV sitcom *Cheers* set?

2

Name the film-making Coen Brothers.

3

Who plays C J Cregg in *The West Wing*?

4

Which Harry Potter film was released in 2007?

5

Who was the first celebrity champion of *Strictly Come Dancing*?

6

Which playwright plays a major role in the film *Get Carter*?

7

Who created The Daleks?

8

Which New Zealand director made *Heavenly Bodies*?

9

Which UK talent show was launched in October 2001?

10

Which film director shares the name of a famous explorer?

11

Who is older, Ant or Dec?

12

Which four Oscar-winning Aussies appeared on postage stamps?

CINEMA & TELEVISION
JAMES BOND MOVIES

1

Which was the first James Bond film?

2

Who sang "Die Another Day" in the film of that name?

3

Who played Bond the most times, Sean Connery or Roger Moore?

4

Who was 007 in *Licence to Kill*?

5

Who was 006 in *GoldenEye*?

6

What nationality is one-time Bond George Lazenby?

7

What is the most destructive thing about Oddjob?

8

What did Donald Pleasence, Telly Savalas and Charles Gray share?

9

In which Bond film did Rowan Atkinson make his big screen debut?

10

Which actor first played "Q"?

11

Who played "Sir James Bond" in the 1967 version of *Casino Royale*?

12

Who was younger on Bond debut, Daniel Craig or Sean Connery?

CINEMA & TELEVISION
MOVIE MUSICALS

1

Who plays Dr Frank N Furter in *The Rocky Horror Picture Show*?

2

What are the rival gangs in *West Side Story*?

3

High Society is a musical remake of which film?

4

Who plays Mrs Banks in *Mary Poppins*?

5

Who wrote the music for *Sweet Charity*?

6

The musical *Guys and Dolls* is based on whose stories?

7

What was Fred Astaire and Ginger Rogers' last film together?

8

Who plays Juan Perón in the film of *Evita*?

9

Which British director won an Oscar for *Oliver!*?

10

In which film is the musical number "Make 'Em Laugh"?

11

Who was originally cast as the male lead in *Easter Parade*?

12

Who plays Roxie Hart's husband in the film *Chicago*?

CINEMA & TELEVISION
TV COOKS

1

What nationality is *Masterchef* presenter John Torode?

2

Which TV chef's parents were both professional actors?

3

Which chef was known on screen as "The Galloping Gourmet"?

4

Who was the UK's first-ever television chef?

5

Who was once head chef at Lord's Cricket Ground?

6

What stuffed Heston Blumenthal's Fat Duck restaurant in 2009?

7

Which football club has to play ball with Delia Smith?

8

Who succeeded Gordon Ramsay in *Hell's Kitchen*?

9

Which TV chef did Fern Britton marry?

10

Which UK chef competed in the gruelling Mille Miglia road race?

11

Which TV chef has a pop group called Scarlet Division?

12

Which of the Two Fat Ladies was formerly a barrister?

CINEMA & TELEVISION
MOVIE TITLES (2): ADD THE PLACE NAMES

1

55 Days at . . .

2

. . . Danny Rose

3

North to . . .

4

The . . . Thunderbolt

5

Five Graves to . . .

6

The Thief of . . .

7

Next Stop . . . Village

8

Les Parapluies de . . .

9

The Black Shield of . . .

10

Last Year at . . .

11

A Night in . . .

12

Thirty Seconds over . . .

CINEMA & TELEVISION
CLINT EASTWOOD AND HIS MOVIES

1

What type of gun does "Dirty Harry" Callahan carry?

2

In which musical Western does Clint Eastwood co-star?

3

What is the name of Eastwood's character in *Unforgiven*?

4

What was Clint Eastwood's first film as director?

5

In which film does Eastwood play a professional thief?

6

In *White Hunter, Black Heart*, who is Eastwood's role based on?

7

Eastwood shot to fame playing who in the TV series *Rawhide*?

8

What political office did Clint Eastwood take on in 1986?

9

In *Space Cowboys*, who played Eastwood's three fellow astronauts?

10

Name Eastwood's long-time female companion and frequent co-star?

11

Who plays Lone Watie in *The Outlaw Josey Wales*?

12

Which three play the "Good", the "Bad" and the "Ugly"?

1

Nicole Kidman won an Oscar for her portrayal of whom in *The Hours*?

2

Which planet was Mork from?

3

Which English film director was knighted in 2002?

4

In which film did Flubber make its first appearance?

5

Who played Charley Farley and Piggy Malone?

6

Who is Fred Flintstone's best friend?

7

Who plays Prince Philip in *The Queen*?

8

What was John Wayne's real name?

9

Who played Tara King in *The Avengers*?

10

What is Julie Walter's role in the Harry Potter films?

11

Which screen comic co-founded United Artists in 1919?

12

Who played Major Winters in *Band of Brothers*?

CINEMA & TELEVISION
ANIMALS ON SCREEN

1

Who does Marcel the monkey belong to?

2

What kind of cat does Blofeld in the Bond movies have?

3

What was the name of Roy Rogers' horse?

4

What is the name of Dorothy's dog in *The Wizard of Oz*?

5

How many spots has Pongo in *101 Dalmations*?

6

What is Elizabeth Taylor's horse is *National Velvet* called?

7

How was a Hollywood male collie called Pal better known?

8

Who leapt to fame in the film *Free Willy*?

9

Which father and son played Eddie in *Frasier*?

10

Who was the cat in the 60s/70s Spillers pet food commercials?

11

What canine breed was Rin Tin Tin?

12

Who was Clint Eastwood's simian pal in *Every Which Way But Loose*?

CINEMA & TELEVISION
TV LOCATIONS

1

What is the seaside setting for *Foyle's War*?

2

In which district of New York is *Friends* set?

3

Where was the cult series *The Prisoner* filmed?

4

Which sitcom is set on an industrial estate in Slough?

5

Which city is home to *Hollyoaks*?

6

Dr Frasier Crane works for a radio station in which US city?

7

Where in Yorkshire is *Last of the Summer Wine* shot?

8

Which London suburb is home to Edina in *Absolutely Fabulous*?

9

Boycie and Marlene find the grass is greener in which county?

10

What is the fictional resort for the happy campers in *Hi-de-Hi*?

11

In *Notting Hill*, where is Julia Roberts shown filming?

12

Inspector George Gently is filmed in which overseas city?

1

Who is singer Ella Edmondson's mother?

2

How were Rita Hayworth and Ginger Rogers related?

3

Which actor's father was UK attorney-general in the 1980s?

4

Who was Thora Hird's film actress daughter?

5

Which husband and wife starred in the TV series *A Fine Romance*?

6

Who was Angelina Jolie's first husband?

7

Michael Sheen's father was a professional lookalike of whom?

8

Who was Catherine Deneuve's film star sister?

9

Helena Bonham-Carter is descended from which UK prime minister?

10

Which two granddaughters of Ernest Hemingway made it into movies?

11

Who is writer Sharman Macdonald's more famous daughter?

12

Dana Andrews was the brother of which fellow Hollywood star?

1

"Shut that door!"

2

"Everybody wants to get into the act."

3

"Just like that."

4

"Write the theme tune, sing the theme tune."

5

"Sock it to me."

6

"Who loves ya, Baby?"

7

"And it's goodnight from him."

8

"He's fallen in the water."

9

"Oh you are awful, but I like you."

10

"I am not a number, I am a free man."

11

"What an absolutely, thoroughly, bloody nice bloke."

12

"Good night, and good luck."

CINEMA & TELEVISION
ALFRED HITCHCOCK MOVIES

1

On whose short story is *The Birds* based?

2

Who plays the private investigator in *Psycho*?

3

Which husband and wife appeared in *Witness for the Prosecution*?

4

Which one of his films did Hitchcock remake in 1956?

5

In *Rear Window,* James Stewart's character does what for a living?

6

Who created the dream sequence in the film *Spellbound*?

7

Which Hitchcock film takes place in Australia?

8

Who played Richard Hannay in *The 39 Steps*?

9

What most concerns Charters and Caldicott in *The Lady Vanishes*?

10

In *Torn Curtain*, Hitchcock makes a brief appearance holding what?

11

Where does the climax to *North by Northwest* take place?

12

What was Hitchcock's last film?

1

In which gangster film did Pierce Brosnan make his screen debut?

2

Who left the house last in the first *Celebrity Big Brother*?

3

Which husband and wife were in the 1994 remake of *The Getaway*?

4

Who directed *The Curious Case of Benjamin Button*?

5

Which foxy character went "Boom! Boom!"?

6

Whose eight minutes on screen were enough for an Oscar in 1998?

7

Which 007 once posed nude for an art class?

8

Which British sitcom was remade in the US as *Three's Company*?

9

What was the first "Carry On" film?

10

What is the top prize at the Cannes Film Festival?

11

On TV, which man behind the wheel prefers to remain anonymous?

12

Who plays Aragorn in *The Lord of the Rings*?

1

What is Switzerland's largest city?

2

San José is the capital of which country?

3

What is fine sediment deposited by a river called?

4

What is England's largest national park?

5

What is the national language of Pakistan?

6

In which US state is Dodge City?

7

To which country do the Azores belong?

8

What name is given to a Scottish peak over 3000ft (914m)?

9

Who is Bolivia named after?

10

Where is the Tsangpo Gorge?

11

On what river does St Petersburg stand?

12

What is the port of Athens?

GEOGRAPHY
ROLLING RIVERS

1

Which is the longest river in Britain?

2

Into which sea does the Mekong river flow?

3

The Kariba Dam is on which African river?

4

On which river does Munich stand?

5

What is France's longest river?

6

The Vistula flows through which capital city?

7

Into which sea does the River Jordan flow?

8

In which country is the source of the White Nile?

9

The Mississippi and Missouri meet near which US city?

10

Hanoi is located on the right bank of which river?

11

The source of the River Thames is in which county?

12

On which river is Perth, Australia?

GEOGRAPHY
MOUNTAINS HIGH

1

Which mountain range divides France and Spain?

2

Mt Elbert is which US mountain range's highest peak?

3

What is the highest mountain in Africa?

4

In which country are the Southern Alps?

5

What is Antarctica's highest mountain?

6

In which country are the Dolomites?

7

What is the highest mountain in Portugal?

8

What is the highest mountain in Europe?

9

What is the world's longest mountain range?

10

Mt Everest stands in which two countries?

11

Which is the highest peak in England?

12

In which country is The Great Dividing Range?

1

Sri Lanka

2

Malawi

3

Belize

4

Bangladesh

5

Thailand

6

Iran

7

Democratic Republic of the Congo

8

Mexico

9

Ghana

10

Kiribati

11

Ethiopia

12

Mali

GEOGRAPHY
GLOBETROTTING (2)

1

Which US state is known as the Diamond State?

2

Which country surrounds San Marino?

3

What is the name of the world's largest gulf?

4

What is the official language of the Ivory Coast?

5

What is the capital of Taiwan?

6

What is England's most southerly mainland point?

7

In which Spanish city is the Alhambra palace?

8

Which is further north, Adelaide or Canberra?

9

What is Japan's highest peak?

10

The Victoria Falls are on which African river?

11

Which US state borders just one other US state?

12

Malta comprises what three inhabited islands?

GEOGRAPHY
WAVING THE FLAG

1

Which country's flag features a maple leaf?

2

What are the colours of the Polish flag?

3

What do the stripes on the US flag represent?

4

How many stars are there on the Chinese national flag?

5

Does the French tricolour have vertical or horizontal stripes?

6

What is the largest star on the Australian flag called?

7

What colours are the German flag, in descending order?

8

Which two symbols are featured on Turkey's national flag?

9

Which country's flag is a solid red circle on a white background?

10

Which UK island's flag features three conjoined legs?

11

What are the colours of the Italian flag, left to right?

12

How many stars are on the flag of the European Union?

GEOGRAPHY
ISLANDS OF THE SEA

1

To which country do the Faroe Islands belong?

2

Which country includes the Isle of Tiree?

3

On which Canadian island is the city of Victoria?

4

Which is New Zealand's larger island, North or South?

5

Kos and Symi are in which group of Greek islands?

6

In which ocean are the Heard and McDonald islands?

7

What is the world's smallest island nation?

8

How many major islands make up the Azores?

9

What is the largest island in Asia?

10

Rarotonga is the capital of which islands?

11

Robinson Crusoe Island lies off the coast of which country?

12

On which island is Tokyo situated?

GEOGRAPHY
LAKES AND LOCHS

. . . .

1

In which country is Lake Garda?

2

Which is the smallest of the Five Great Lakes?

3

Which two South American countries border Lake Titicaca?

4

Which is the world's deepest lake?

5

What is Scotland's largest loch?

6

On which New Zealand island is Lake Taupo?

7

Which country has the minority share of Lake Geneva?

8

In which US mountain range is Lake Tahoe situated?

9

Which four US states border Lake Erie?

10

What is the world's largest lake?

11

Which is England's second largest natural lake?

12

What lake is the lowest point in Australia?

1

Where in India is the Taj Mahal?

2

Where will you find the ancient ruins of Carthage?

3

What is the name of the most famous bridge in Florence?

4

In which country are the Shakta Pantjukhina caves?

5

Which four US presidents can be seen at Mount Rushmore?

6

Which New Zealand city is known for its geothermal activity?

7

The Giant's Causeway is in which Irish county?

8

Uluru is the aboriginal name for what?

9

What is the largest sand dune in Europe?

10

The Reichenbach Falls are in which country?

11

In which famous square is St Basil's Cathedral?

12

In which country is Machu Picchu?

GEOGRAPHY
GLOBETROTTING (3)

1

Which two countries does the Simplon Tunnel link?

2

What is the second longest river in the world?

3

What is the capital of Estonia?

4

In which South American country is Lake Maracaibo?

5

What three countries border Luxembourg?

6

In which US national park is the geyser "Old Faithful"?

7

What is the world's longest canal?

8

Which major river has its source in the Black Forest?

9

What is the smallest of the Channel Islands open to the public?

10

New Caledonia is an overseas territory of which European country?

11

What mountain range broadly separates Europe from Asia?

12

Where are the Spanish Steps?

1

What does occidental mean?

2

Which is longer, a nautical mile or a land mile?

3

In which hemisphere is the Tropic of Cancer?

4

What is the meeting of two rivers called?

5

What is measured on the Richter Scale?

6

What is a large, flat-topped landform with steep rocky walls?

7

What is a cataract?

8

What is a group of islands called?

9

What word describes a shallow lake of salt water?

10

What is chorology?

11

What is molten rock below the earth's crust called?

12

What is a wadi?

1

Which ocean covers more than a third of the earth's surface?

2

The Bass Strait separates which two areas of land?

3

Where are the highest tides in the world recorded?

4

Which sea has the highest concentration of salt?

5

What is the world's smallest ocean?

6

What links the Mediterranean Sea to the Atlantic Ocean?

7

Which sea is located north of Norway and Russia?

8

In which sea is the Great Barrier Reef?

9

Which two gulfs are linked by the Strait of Hormuz?

10

Which ocean has the deepest point?

11

Which strait connects the Pacific and Atlantic oceans?

12

Which sea lies between Sardinia and mainland Italy?

GEOGRAPHY
DESERT LANDSCAPES

58

1

What is the driest inhabited continent on Earth?

2

What mountain range is to the north of the Sahara?

3

By which other name is the Great Indian Desert known?

4

What is the world's largest desert?

5

Which two countries share the Gobi Desert?

6

In what US state is the Colorado Desert?

7

What percentage of Egypt is desert?

8

The Kalahari Desert spans which two African countries?

9

Which desert contains the driest place on Earth?

10

In which Australian state is the Great Sandy Desert?

11

In which desert will you find the Joshua tree?

12

Which Chinese desert is known as the "Sea of Death"?

GEOGRAPHY
CAPITAL CITIES

1

What became the new capital of Germany in 1999?

2

By what name was Harare previously known?

3

What is the capital of Florida?

4

Bratislava is the capital of which European country?

5

How is Te Whanganui-a-Tara better known?

6

What is the capital of Paraguay?

7

What is the most northerly capital in the world?

8

What is the provincial capital of Saskatchewan in Canada?

9

North Dakota's capital is the name of which German statesman?

10

Which capital is on the Potomac river?

11

What is the capital of Rwanda?

12

What is the highest capital city in the world?

GEOGRAPHY
GLOBETROTTING (4)

1

What is the longest enclosed glen in Scotland?

2

What US state is nicknamed the "Beaver State"?

3

What is the capital of Ecuador?

4

Which two countries are separated by the Kattegat?

5

What is the largest city in the Crimea?

6

Which English city was once known as *Deva*?

7

What are the Moluccan Islands also known as?

8

In what country is the spa town of Spa?

9

Scapa Flow is in which group of islands?

10

What is the port of Perth in Western Australia?

11

The porcelain-making town of Meissen stands on which river?

12

Which is Europe's highest capital city?

61

GEOGRAPHY

NAME THEIR CURRENCY

1
South Africa

2
Vietnam

3
Israel

4
Cuba

5
Egypt

6
China

7
Russia

8
South Korea

9
Switzerland

10
Brazil

11
Denmark

12
Mongolia

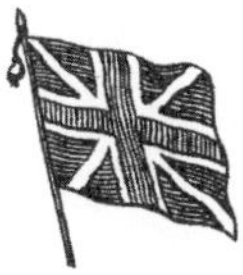

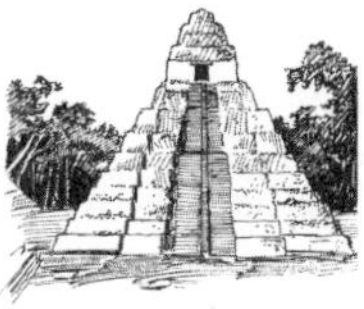

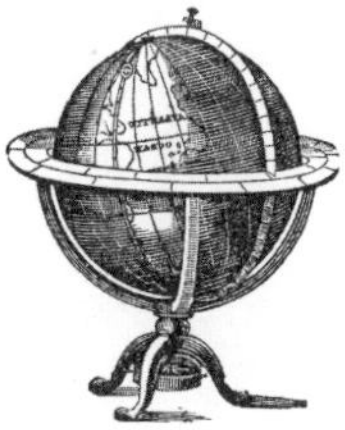

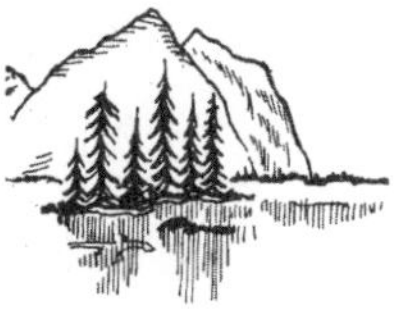

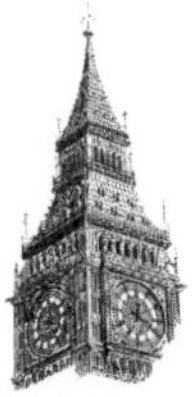

1

What is Chicago's major airport?

2

Schiphol is which city's airport?

3

How was New York's JFK airport previously known?

4

What is the Scottish capital's airport?

5

Which British architect designed the new Madrid airport?

6

What is the name of Hong Kong's international airport?

7

Which city's airport was previously called Kingsford-Smith?

8

Where was London's first airport?

9

After which famous explorer is Venice's airport named?

10

Chhatrapati Shivaji airport serves which Indian city?

11

Which Canadian airport is named after a former prime minister?

12

Where is Narita International Airport?

GEOGRAPHY
HOW WERE THESE PREVIOUSLY KNOWN? (2)

1
Beijing

2
Gdańsk

3
Ho Chi Minh City

4
New York

5
Dhaka

6
Oslo

7
Maputo

8
Istanbul

9
Nizhny Novgorod

10
Tokyo

11
Mumbai

12
Kinshasa

GEOGRAPHY
BRITISH ISLES

64

1

Which is mainland Britain's most northern town?

2

On which river does the city of Ely stand?

3

Which is the UK's third largest city?

4

Can you name the original Cinque Ports?

5

What is the largest of London's subterranean rivers?

6

By what other name is Holy Island known?

7

Which is Scotland's longest river?

8

What is the largest prehistoric monument in England?

9

Which major underground cave was discovered in England in 2006?

10

What is the largest lake in the British Isles?

11

Tobermory is on which Scottish island?

12

Glevum was the Roman name for which English city?

GEOGRAPHY
GLOBETROTTING (5)

1

Ben Nevis is in which mountain range?

2

How is the Greek island of Kerkyra better known?

3

In which other country does London stand on the River Thames?

4

What was the original name of Boston, Massachusetts?

5

What two rivers merge to become the Shatt-al-Arab?

6

On how many hills is Rome built?

7

Which country's flag is solid green?

8

In which country is Transylvania?

9

New Britain and Admiralty are in which Pacific group of islands?

10

What is Canada's highest mountain?

11

What is the largest city within the Arctic Circle?

12

Where is Timbuktu?

1

How many Crusades were there?

2

Which war ended with the Treaty of Panmunjom?

3

In which battle did the Sioux defeat General Custer?

4

Who was The War of Jenkin's Ear between?

5

In which war was the Battle of Brandywine Creek?

6

Who was defeated at Dien Bien Phu in 1954?

7

When was the Battle of Culloden?

8

What war came to an end in August 1988?

9

How long did the Hundred Years War last?

10

Which war concluded with the 1713 Treaty of Utrecht?

11

What was the shelling of Fort Sumter the start of?

12

Who was the Peloponnesian War between?

HISTORY
WORLD WAR I

1

Whose assassination in Sarajevo in 1914 led to the war?

2

How were French soldiers transported to the battle of the Marne?

3

Who was British prime minister at the outbreak of the war?

4

Who was appointed Allied Commander in Chief in 1918?

5

What armoured vehicle made its first appearance during the war?

6

Who wrote the poem "Suicide in the Trenches"?

7

What military campaign gave birth to ANZAC Day?

8

To which country did Kaiser Wilhelm II flee in 1918?

9

What did George V pledge to give up at the start of the war?

10

Who commanded the US Expeditionary Force?

11

Who became known as the "Butcher of the Somme"?

12

Who were known as the "Old Contemptibles"?

1

"History is bunk."

2

"All I know is that I am not a Marxist."

3

"The one duty we owe to history is to rewrite it."

4

"Is Paris burning?"

5

"Published and be damned!"

6

"Your president is no crook."

7

"The ballot is stronger than the bullet."

8

"England is a nation of shopkeepers."

9

"You've never had it so good."

10

"I will make you shorter by a head."

11

"How can a president not be an actor?"

12

"If we lose this war, I'll start another in my wife's name."

HISTORY
PAST TIMES (1)

1

Which country became part of Great Britain in 1801?

2

What did George Shillibeer introduce to London in 1829?

3

What was the world's first skyscraper?

4

Where did Alexander the Great die?

5

Which was the first republic in Western Europe?

6

Which civilization built Machu Picchu?

7

Who was the first Protestant Archbishop of Canterbury?

8

What was the name of Lord Nelson's daughter by Lady Hamilton?

9

Where was the Magna Carta signed in 1215?

10

For how many years did Queen Victoria reign?

11

What institution did George Williams found in London in 1844?

12

In which year did the Vietnam War end?

HISTORY
YEARS TO REMEMBER

1

In which year did the Russian Revolution begin?

2

When was NATO founded?

3

When was the Great Fire of London?

4

What year was the Lockerbie air disaster?

5

In which year did Saddam Hussein become president of Iraq?

6

When was the "Six Day" Arab-Israeli war?

7

In which year was Britain's only general strike?

8

When did the Berlin Wall come down?

9

When was the "Boston Tea Party" protest?

10

When was Nelson Mandela released from prison?

11

When was the Irish Free State established?

12

In which year was Mahatma Gandhi assassinated?

HISTORY
KINGS AND QUEENS

1

What relation was Queen Victoria to George IV?

2

Who was the father of the last tsar of Russia?

3

Which king of England was crowned on Christmas Day?

4

Which French king was guillotined in 1793?

5

Who was the mother of Edward VI?

6

Which British king was the last Emperor of India?

7

Who was the first British monarch to abdicate?

8

What nationality was French queen Marie Antoinette?

9

Which king of England was "the wisest fool in Christendom"?

10

Which Egyptian king abdicated in 1952?

11

Who became Saudi Arabia's first king in 1932?

12

How many of Queen Anne's five children survived her?

HISTORY
BRITISH PRIME MINISTERS

1

For how many years was Margaret Thatcher prime minister?

2

Who was Britain's only illegitimate prime minister?

3

What was Harold Wilson's title when he became a peer?

4

Which prime minister wrote the novel *Vivian Grey*?

5

Which British prime minister was assassinated in 1812?

6

Who was prime minister during Edward VIII's abdication?

7

How old was William Pitt when he became prime minister in 1783?

8

How many times was William Gladstone prime minister?

9

Which 20th-century British prime minister was born in Canada?

10

What is Gordon Brown's first name?

11

Who was known as the "Welsh Wizard"?

12

Name the only prime minister to have played first class cricket.

1

When was the Bay of Pigs invasion of Cuba?

2

Who was the first American to orbit the earth?

3

Which British national daily newspaper was launched in 1965?

4

Who was the American U2 pilot captured by the Russians?

5

Whose book *Silent Spring* launched the environmental movement?

6

Which black American leader was assassinated in 1965?

7

In what year was the first Notting Hill Carnival?

8

Which writing instrument was launched in Japan in 1960?

9

What was the 1968 revolution in Czechoslovakia called?

10

Who became Israel's first female prime minister in 1969?

11

What was introduced onto London streets in 1961?

12

In which country was Che Guevara killed in 1967?

1

Vladimir Illyich Ulyanov

2

Manfred von Richthofen

3

Malcolm Little

4

Dolores Ibarruri

5

Siddhartha Gautama

6

Thomas Edward Lawrence

7

Agnes Gonxha Bojaxhiu

8

Rodrigo Diaz de Vivar

9

William Joyce

10

Lev Davidovitch Bronstein

11

Saloth Sar

12

Josip Broz

HISTORY
PAST TIMES (2)

1

In which year did the New York City Subway open?

2

Who wrote *The Rights of Man*?

3

What did Eire leave in 1949?

4

What was the name of Dick Turpin's horse?

5

When was the English pound note withdrawn?

6

What year did the UK's first public library open?

7

Who was the first woman to fly the Atlantic solo?

8

Who founded the Christian Science movement?

9

Which country did Russia invade in 1956?

10

During the Boer War who was known as "Uncle Paul"?

11

Which sheriff killed Billy the Kid?

12

What nationality was the spy Mata Hari?

1

Of which country was King Zog the ruler?

2

Which queen of Tonga attended Elizabeth II's coronation in 1953?

3

The Black Prince was the son of which English king?

4

Who was the second wife divorced by Henry VIII?

5

How many kings of France were named Louis?

6

Of which English tribe was Queen Boadicea the ruler?

7

Name the first British monarch of the House of Saxe-Coburg-Gotha.

8

Who was the last king of Italy?

9

Who did James VI of Scotland become?

10

What is Queen Elizabeth II's date of birth?

11

Which queen is said to have written the "Casket Letters"?

12

Which Russian tsar was assassinated in 1881?

1

Who was Blackbeard the pirate?

2

Who was the first UN Secretary General?

3

Was Abraham Lincoln a Republican or a Democrat?

4

What did the USA purchase from Russia in 1867?

5

Who was the only English pope to date?

6

"Traveller" was which American Civil War general's horse?

7

Which is the world's oldest parliament?

8

In which century was the Taj Mahal built?

9

Where in 1914 was the world's first traffic light installed?

10

Who was Tsar Nicholas II's youngest daughter?

11

Which island was awarded the George Cross in 1942?

12

Who was the first English Christian martyr?

. . . .

1

Which Marxist became president of Chile in 1970?

2

What was banned from US television in 1971?

3

Who in 1972 became the first US president to visit China?

4

What honour was bestowed on Charlie Chaplin in 1975?

5

Which female received the 1979 Nobel Peace Prize?

6

Which US vice-president was forced to resign in 1973?

7

When did McDonald's open its first fast-food outlet in London?

8

Who was the UK's first female television newsreader?

9

Which US heiress was kidnapped by the Symbionese Liberation Army?

10

Who became president of Uganda in 1971?

11

Who was stripped of his knighthood in 1979 for spying?

12

Which UK prime minister introduced the three-day working week?

1

In which year was John F Kennedy assassinated?

2

When did man first walk on the moon?

3

In which year was the Japanese attack on Pearl Harbor?

4

When was the Battle of the Somme?

5

When was decimal currency introduced in the UK?

6

When did Argentina invade the Falkland Islands?

7

When was the partitioning of India and Pakistan?

8

When did the Californian Gold Rush begin?

9

In which year did Queen Victoria come to the throne?

10

Charles I was executed on 30 January of which year?

11

In what year was the siege of Mafeking relieved?

12

When was the Charge of the Light Brigade?

1

Which two great military adversaries were born in 1769?

2

Hannibal led which army across the Alps?

3

Who commanded the Dambusters squadron?

4

Who was the victorious English general at the Battle of Blenheim?

5

Who was known as "Stormin' Norman"?

6

Who was the commander-in-chief of allied forces on D-Day?

7

Who led the English to victory at Crécy and Poitiers?

8

Which Civil War general became 18th president of the US?

9

In which county of England was Horatio Nelson born?

10

Who was the victorious Red Army commander at Stalingrad?

11

How many enemy aircraft did Douglas Bader shoot down in WWII?

12

Who captured Quebec in 1759 and died in the process?

1

What was Richard Nixon's middle name?

2

Who succeeded Gerald Ford as president?

3

Which president was assassinated in 1881?

4

Which president was the first occupant of the White House?

5

"Monticello" was the home of which president?

6

Who was the first unmarried president?

7

Mary Todd was the wife of which president?

8

Which president died of a chill caught on Inauguration Day?

9

Which president was nicknamed "Old Hickory"?

10

Who was president at the end of World War II?

11

Which two former presidents died on the same day in 1826?

12

Who did George W Bush defeat in the 2004 presidential election?

HISTORY
FAMOUS EXPLORERS

1

In which ship did Francis Drake circumnavigate the world?

2

When did Christopher Columbus discover the New World?

3

Where is David Livingstone buried?

4

Who led the first crossing of Antarctica in 1958?

5

Which country did Robert Burke and William Wills explore?

6

Who opened the first sea route to India?

7

In which country was the explorer H M Stanley born?

8

Which European explorer served the Mongol emperor Kublai Khan?

9

What was third time lucky for Ranulph Fiennes in 2009?

10

Which British explorer translated the *Kama Sutra*?

11

Which African river did Mungo Park chart?

12

Who was America named after?

HISTORY
NICKNAMES

83

1

Who was the "Iron Duke"?

2

Who was Supermac?

3

Who was known as the "Scourge of God"?

4

Who was "Papa Doc"?

5

Who was the "Little Corporal"?

6

Which general was known as the "Desert Fox"?

7

Which French prime minister was nicknamed "Tiger"?

8

Who was called "Old Blood and Guts" by his troops?

9

Who was known as the "Hanging Judge"?

10

Who was the "Iron Chancellor"?

11

Who was the "Sun King"?

12

Who was called the "Hammer of the Scots"?

1

What was the name of the first US space shuttle?

2

Which London embassy was seized by terrorists in 1980?

3

Who murdered John Lennon?

4

What did Australia celebrate in 1988?

5

What spilled 11 million gallons of oil in Alaska?

6

In what year was the Chernobyl nuclear disaster?

7

Who was the president of Austria with a Nazi past?

8

Who did George Bush defeat in the 1988 US election?

9

Which country did the US invade in 1983?

10

Who became French president in 1981?

11

What made its first appearance on Soviet TV in 1988?

12

In what year was 19 October "Black Monday"?

HISTORY
WORLD WAR II

1

What was Operation Sealion?

2

Who invented the Dambusters' bomb?

3

What rank was Hermann Goering?

4

Who commanded the British forces in Burma?

5

In which year was the battle of El Alamein?

6

Which Nazi flew to Scotland on a secret mission in 1941?

7

What was the Maquis?

8

Which two UK ministers had air-raid shelters named after them?

9

Who retreated with the words, "I shall return"?

10

Who became the first-ever combat soldier to win a double VC?

11

Who headed the Vichy government in France?

12

How old was Adolf Hitler when he died?

1

Whose face is said to have launched a thousand ships?

2

Which Roman emperor appointed his horse a consul?

3

Who founded the Persian Empire?

4

Which ancient city did Pericles rule?

5

Whose wall stretches from Newcastle to Carlisle?

6

Who was the Roman god of fire?

7

In which country was Alexander the Great born?

8

Which gladiator led a slave revolt against the Romans?

9

How was the Greek philosopher Socrates made to take his own life?

10

Which Roman general wrote a history of the Gallic Wars?

11

Who was the Battle of Marathon in 490BC between?

12

Who was considered the greatest of all Roman orators?

HISTORY
PAST TIMES (4)

1

Where was London's Great Exhibition of 1851 held?

2

Whose mistress was Clara Petacci?

3

What did Howard Carter and Lord Carnarvon find in 1922?

4

How did suffragette martyr Emily Davison die in 1913?

5

Who was excommunicated at the Diet of Worms?

6

Who ruled England after Oliver Cromwell?

7

In which century did the "Black Death" decimate Europe?

8

What was code-named Operation Dynamo in World War Two?

9

In which city was outlaw Ned Kelly hanged in 1880?

10

Who founded the Turkish Republic ?

11

Which Chinese dynasty came first, Ming or Qing?

12

What mail service was used during the 1870 siege of Paris?

1

Who sang "Something Stupid" with Robbie Williams?

2

"A Whole New World" was the hope of which tabloid couple in 2006?

3

Which sexy couple had their 1969 hit banned by the BBC?

4

In which country were The Cheeky Girls born?

5

Bryan Adams sang "When You're Gone" with Mel C – then with whom?

6

Which 70s male/female duo found fame via *Opportunity Knocks*?

7

The Oscar-winning "When You Believe" was sung by which star duo?

8

Which duo wrote Peter and Gordon's 60s hit "World Without Love"?

9

Which amphibian sang with Kylie Minogue on her show in 2001?

10

Which Israeli couple had a No 1 hit in the UK in 1968?

11

What nationality were Nina and Frederick?

12

Who are The Kills?

MUSIC
WHO DID THEY BECOME?

1

Michael Barrett

2

Barry Pincus

3

Christopher John Davidson

4

Seymour

5

Cordoza Calvin Broadus Jr

6

Harry Webb

7

Annie Mae Bullock

8

Marvin Lee Aday

9

Reg Smith

10

Steven Demetre Georgiou

11

The Paramounts

12

Terry Nelhams

MUSIC
THE BEATLES

90

1

Who were John, Paul and George before The Beatles?

2

Which major record company rejected The Beatles in 1962?

3

For whom did Paul McCartney write "Hey Jude"?

4

Which two Beatles were left-handed?

5

Which Beatle sang backing vocals on Donovan's "Mellow Yellow"?

6

With which Beatles' song did The Overlanders reach No 1 in 1966?

7

What was the name of John Lennon's cat?

8

Who parodied the lyrics of "A Hard Day's Night" as Richard III?

9

"Baby You're A Rich Man" is dedicated to whom?

10

Bernard Webb was the pseudonym of which Beatle?

11

The Beatles made their first live US performance on what TV show?

12

What was The Beatles' last UK No 1?

MUSIC
POP GOES CHRISTMAS

1

Who had a mega hit in 1973 with "Merry Christmas Everybody"?

2

What was Johnny Mathis's 1976 Christmas offering?

3

Which group were "Alone On Christmas Day" in 2004?

4

Which was the first Christmas song to make it to No 1 in the UK?

5

"Christmas Is Just Around The Corner" was a 2008 hit for whom?

6

Who was the first of many to record "The Christmas Waltz"?

7

In which year did Band Aid produce their first Christmas record?

8

What Christmas song has a dental theme?

9

Which ex-Beatle recorded "Ding Dong, Ding Dong"?

10

"Have Yourself A Merry Little Christmas" comes from which film?

11

Which Bobby Darin song combined Christmas and New Year?

12

What was Cliff Richard's Christmas song for 2003?

1

"That Girl Belongs To Yesterday" was a hit for which US singer?

2

Which Cambridge graduate sang "Everyone's Gone To The Moon"?

3

What are the Everly Brothers' first names?

4

Who sang about the Texan town of Galveston?

5

Name the Rolling Stones' first US No 1 in 1965?

6

In which year did Elvis Presley get married?

7

How old was Helen Shapiro when she recorded her first hit?

8

In 1968, who covered Tony Bennett's hit "For Once In My Life"?

9

Who had a 60s hit with "The Boat That I Row"?

10

Which Beach Boy was acquitted of draft evasion in 1967?

11

Which 60s group was made up of two pairs of sisters?

12

In 1966, which father and daughter each had a UK No 1?

1

Which Scottish singer used to work in a frozen fish factory?

2

What is Paul McCartney's first name?

3

Who did David Essex play on stage in *Evita*?

4

How many were there originally in the Spice Girls?

5

What is the name of Russia's foremost ballet company?

6

Which popular US singer died in 2007, aged 93?

7

Which English city is Engelbert Humperdinck from?

8

Which UK pop star made a point of performing in bare feet?

9

Who was the first black soloist to sing at the New York Met?

10

Which rock star once worked as a gravedigger?

11

Who had a hit in 1972 with "Puppy Love"?

12

Which singer is known as "The Queen of Soul"?

1

"Here Comes The Judge" was whose only UK hit?

2

"Let's Go To San Francisco" was whose hit idea in 1967?

3

Who in 1966 claimed "They're Coming To Take Me Away, Ha-Haaa!"?

4

What was the name of Doop's 1994 hit?

5

Which comedy duo had their only hit with "The Stonk" in 1991?

6

Which TV actor sang in character for his hit "Grandad"?

7

What was B Bumble and the Stingers' 1962 hit?

8

Which gravel-voiced movie actor made it with "Wanderin' Star"?

9

Who had four weeks at No 1 with "Sugar Sugar" in 1969?

10

"She's About A Mover" was which US toff band's 1965 hit?

11

How did the Teletubbies clock over a million sales?

12

"Matchstalk Men & Matchstalk Cats & Dogs" was a tribute to whom?

95

MUSIC
COLOUR THESE SONGS

1

"The . . . Rose Of Texas"

2

"Paint It . . ."

3

"Shades Of . . ."

4

"Mood . . ."

5

". . . Dressed For Sunset"

6

"Lily The . . ."

7

". . . Is The Colour, Football Is The Game"

8

". . . Rain"

9

". . . Shirt"

10

"My Love Is . . ."

11

"Symphony In . . ."

12

"Fields Of . . ."

1

Who was Sid Vicious's girlfriend?

2

Which group had a hit with "Good Morning Judge"?

3

In 1972 the Partridge Family covered which Neil Sedaka hit?

4

What was the first UK No 1 for Marc Bolan and T Rex?

5

How old was Jimi Hendrix when he died in 1970?

6

What was Michael Jackson's first solo record?

7

What was Status Quo's first and only No 1 hit single?

8

The Eagles was originally the backing group for which singer?

9

Which Donna Summer song did the BBC ban in 1976?

10

In what year did Elvis Presley die?

11

How many people were in The Village People?

12

Carly Simon's 1972 hit "You're So Vain" is dedicated to whom?

MUSIC
MUSICAL MEDLEY (2)

1

Which group backed Buddy Holly?

2

What is Ozzy Osbourne's real name?

3

What was the last album The Beatles recorded?

4

Where is the home of the world-famous Concertgebouw Orchestra?

5

Who had a 1980s No 1 with "Move Closer"?

6

Who composed the album "Tubular Bells"?

7

What instrument did Glenn Miller play?

8

Whose follies went from Broadway to Hollywood?

9

Which film featured the single "Vogue" by Madonna?

10

Who wrote the music for the song "Jerusalem"?

11

What was John Lennon's middle name?

12

Who wrote the words, Gilbert or Sullivan?

MUSIC
ALL THAT JAZZ

1

Which popular English jazz musician died in 2008?

2

What instrument did Miles Davis play?

3

Which jazz musician was known as "Bird"?

4

Which big-band leader disappeared on a flight to France in 1944?

5

Who was "Empress of the Blues"?

6

"Pops" was one of his nicknames – what was the other?

7

Who was the "King of Swing"?

8

Which iconic jazz singer was a former prostitute?

9

Who are the "Duke", the "Earl" and the "Count"?

10

Which jazz quartet got into the charts with "Take Five"?

11

Who played tenor sax at his own London jazz club?

12

Which 1950s film did wonders for the Newport Jazz Festival?

MUSIC
UNDER THE BATON

1

Which former jazz pianist became principal conductor of the LSO?

2

Which conductor founded the "Proms"?

3

Who conducts the orchestra in the Disney film *Fantasia*?

4

Which symphony orchestra did Eugene Ormandy conduct for 44 years?

5

Which conductor of the Hallé Orchestra died in 1970?

6

Which conductor founded the London Philharmonic in 1932?

7

In which city was Sir Simon Rattle born?

8

Which legendary conductor was born in Salzburg in 1908?

9

Which UK prime minister conducted on the concert platform?

10

Which US musician was equally famous as conductor and composer?

11

Which English conductor had a 75th birthday concert in 2009?

12

Who won the final of the first *Maestro* competition on TV?

MUSIC
POP GOES THE 80s

1

Who recorded the 1982 hit "Pass The Dutchie"?

2

What was *Spitting Image*'s nonsensical hit in 1986?

3

In which year did Wham split up?

4

Who played in The Jam and Style Council before going solo?

5

How old was *Top of the Pops* in 1989?

6

In which 1987 film is Dean Martin's "That's Amore" featured?

7

What George Michael number was banned from the BBC in 1987?

8

"Like A Virgin" was the unlikely named hit album for whom?

9

Who was Billy Joel singing about in "Uptown Girl"?

10

Bucks Fizz won the 1981 Eurovision Song Contest with what song?

11

What was Kylie Minogue's first No 1 in the UK?

12

What was U2's only UK No 1 single in the 1980s?

1

Who was the singer with Roxy Music?

2

Which instrument did jazz musician John Coltrane play?

3

Who composed *The Love For Three Oranges*?

4

Who wrote the lyrics for the song "Hakuna Matata"?

5

What does the Japanese word *karaoke* mean?

6

Which 70s pop group regrouped for the 2007 Grammys?

7

Which film introduced the song "White Christmas"?

8

Who wrote the song "Keep The Home Fires Burning"?

9

What ecclesiastical group made the classical charts in 2008?

10

Who did Reese Witherspoon play in the biopic *Walk the Line*?

11

Who died first, Gilbert or Sullivan?

12

Who were the song and dance duo of the stage show *Viva la Diva*?

1

Who composed the *Star Wars* theme?

2

Which musical instrument is featured in *The Third Man*?

3

In which film is the song "Windmills of Your Mind"?

4

Whose music for *Atonement* won an Oscar in 2008?

5

Who composed the music for *Million Dollar Baby*?

6

Who sang the theme song from the Bond movie *Licence to Kill*?

7

What do the POWs whistle in *The Bridge Over the River Kwai*?

8

Whose music accompanied *The Sting*?

9

Who was the Oscar-winning composer for *Chariots of Fire*?

10

"I Need To Wake Up" was the wake-up call in which film?

11

Who wrote the *Pink Panther* theme?

12

Which composer do *Dr Zhivago* and *Lawrence of Arabia* share?

1

The opera *William Tell* was written by which composer?

2

Which famous European opera house was founded in 1778?

3

How many operas comprise Wagner's Ring cycle?

4

In the world of opera, what is a diva?

5

Who wrote the opera *The Tales of Hoffmann*?

6

What do the initials stand for in W S Gilbert?

7

How is the character Cio-Cio San better known?

8

Which Benjamin Britten opera is from a story by Herman Melville?

9

In the opera of the same name, what is Tosca's profession?

10

What is the text of an opera called?

11

Which great female opera singer was born in Sydney in 1926?

12

Which two Verdi operas are based on Shakespearean characters?

1

Peter and the Wolf

2

Carnival of the Animals

3

Young Person's Guide to the Orchestra

4

Arrival of the Queen of Sheba

5

Bolero

6

Appalachian Spring

7

Clair de Lune

8

Enigma Variations

9

The Stars and Stripes Forever

10

Academic Festival Overture

11

The Swan of Tuonela

12

On Hearing the First Cuckoo in Spring

1

Who shot to fame with their debut single "MmmmBop"?

2

Who wrote Sinéad O'Connor's 1990 hit "Nothing Compares 2 U"?

3

What acting duo recorded The Bachelors' song "I Believe"?

4

"Tuesday Night Music Club" was a 90s hit for whom?

5

What was the name of Annie Lennox's solo debut album?

6

What was Jamiroquai's 1993 debut album called?

7

Where does The Verve hail from?

8

Who became a Lieutenant of the Royal Victorian Order in 1994?

9

Who appeared as JD in *Lock, Stock and Two Smoking Barrels*?

10

Who had the No 1 album hit "OK Computer" in 1997?

11

"Love Is All Around" by Wet Wet Wet is in which 1994 film?

12

Joe Cocker's "Delta Lady" is dedicated to which singer?

1

Who composed the music for the ballet *Coppélia*?

2

Who is singer Nora Jones's famous father?

3

In the song, which river is "wider than a mile"?

4

Which hit for The Shadows is also a balsa raft?

5

What nationality was singer Jacques Brel?

6

Who is Elton John's long-time lyricist?

7

Larry Hagman is the son of which musical star?

8

What rap group recorded the hit album *Licensed to Kill*?

9

Who was the drummer in The Monkees?

10

In which film did Elvis Presley play a boxer?

11

"Twentysomething" was which UK jazz artist's 2003 debut album?

12

Which country gave birth to Dame Kiri Te Kanawa?

1

Beethoven's fifth piano concerto is known as what?

2

Which 18th-century composer wrote more than 100 symphonies?

3

Who wrote "The Four Seasons"?

4

The "New World Symphony" is number what by Dvořák?

5

How many children did Johann Sebastian Bach have?

6

Which Rachmaninov piano concerto featured in *Brief Encounter*?

7

How many keys on a standard piano?

8

How many movements are there in Gustav Holst's "Planets Suite"?

9

How old was Mozart when he died?

10

Which Mahler symphony was used for the film *Death in Venice*?

11

How many "Pomp and Circumstance" marches did Elgar compose?

12

What does Tchaikovsky's "1812 Overture" celebrate?

1

Who was the founder of Island Records?

2

With which band did Sandy Denny make her name?

3

Which 1960s pop group had a flautist up front?

4

Which Jamaican singer starred in the film *The Harder They Come*?

5

In which year did Robbie Williams leave Take That?

6

Which 1970s pop group had the name of a US bomber?

7

Whose debut solo album was titled "Faith"?

8

An assassination attempt was made on which singer's life in 1976?

9

Which group declared in 1979 "Video Killed The Radio Star"?

10

Who wrote and sang the theme for the film *Absolute Beginners*?

11

The BBC banned which 80s hit by Frankie Goes to Hollywood?

12

Which iconic US rock festival took place in 1969?

1

What was the first solo British hit for Cher?

2

In which city did Jim Morrison of The Doors die?

3

Where in New York was the original Cotton Club?

4

Who wrote the music for the film *The Magnificent Seven*?

5

Is That It? is the autobiography of which pop star?

6

What ageless song did Mildred and Patty Hill write in 1893?

7

Which pop star formed the Notting Hillbillies?

8

What musical instrument did comedian Jack Benny play?

9

Who was the vocalist in Genesis before Phil Collins?

10

On which instrument would you play a paradiddle-diddle?

11

Who sang the theme from the Bond film *From Russia with Love*?

12

How is French pianist Philippe Pages better known?

110

PEOPLE
ALL SORTS (1)

1

Which Dennis created *The Singing Detective*?

2

Who said: "Genius is 99% perspiration and 1% inspiration"?

3

Ed McBain and Evan Hunter are pen names of which US writer?

4

Which Russian dissident won the Nobel Peace Prize in 1975?

5

Which Irish playwright co-founded the London School of Economics?

6

Who was the fourth US president?

7

What were the surnames of Bonnie and Clyde?

8

Who in 2009 was appointed the UK's Chief Scout?

9

Which French aviator has a sports stadium named after him?

10

Who was the first man to reach the South Pole?

11

Which UK prime minister's wife was a published poet?

12

What do the initials in A A Gill stand for?

PEOPLE
WHICH GEORGE?

1

Which George broke up with Andrew Ridgeley in 1986?

2

Which George wrote *St Joan*?

3

Which George commanded the Continental Army in 1775?

4

Which George was Flash Harry at St Trinian's?

5

Which George's real name was Amandine Aurore Lucile Dupin?

6

Which George did an intruder stab at his home in 1999?

7

Which George has an airport named after him?

8

Which George wrote the music while his brother wrote the words?

9

Which George was engaged to Linda Ronstadt?

10

Which George created a plan for Europe after World War II?

11

Which George directed the film *Shane*?

12

Which George raised £10 million for Darfur?

1

Which was Princess Margaret's favourite holiday destination?

2

Which royal princess wrote *The Serpent and the Moon*?

3

Which new royal was born on 23 March 1990?

4

Who was the first royal to be interviewed on TV?

5

Whose dog killed one of the Queen's corgis in 2003?

6

Who was prime minister at the time of the Queen's Silver Jubilee?

7

Which royal qualified as an architect in 1970?

8

When is Prince William's birthday?

9

In which year was The Prince's Trust founded?

10

Which royal couple was divorced in 1996?

11

What is Prince Harry's full name?

12

With which stage star was Prince Edward romantically involved?

1

Who was the first man to fly solo across the Atlantic?

2

Who was the first woman to become a member of Parliament?

3

Who was the first athlete to run a mile in under four minutes?

4

Who was the first monarch to reside at Buckingham Palace?

5

Who was the first woman in space?

6

Who was the first prime minister of Israel?

7

Who was the first person to speak on the telephone?

8

Who was the first professional to captain England at cricket?

9

Who was the first Tudor monarch?

10

Who was the first female speaker of the US House of Representatives?

11

Who was the first person to sail solo around the world?

12

Who was the first to swim the English Channel?

1

Who was the high-profile wife of Mikhail Gorbachev?

2

Who was America's first First Lady?

3

Which presidential wife dated Eric Clapton and Mick Jagger?

4

Which US president's wife was named Rosalynn?

5

Which presidential wife was an obsessive collector of shoes?

6

Which ex-wife of a president was sentenced to jail in 2003?

7

Which US First Lady was a successful business entrepreneur?

8

Which wife of a president had a musical written about her?

9

Which presidential widow took up a career in publishing?

10

Which First Lady founded her own rehab centre?

11

Which president's wife was executed with her husband in 1989?

12

Who became a UN delegate after she left the White House?

PEOPLE
ALL SORTS (2)

1

Which controversial US comedian died of an overdose in 1966?

2

Who was John the Baptist's father?

3

Which pioneer aviatrix was drowned parachuting into the Thames?

4

Who wrote "The Battle Hymn of the Republic"?

5

What does the W stand for in George W Bush?

6

Who pioneered frozen foods in the USA?

7

Which English science-fiction writer was nicknamed "DNA"?

8

Who designed a push-up bra for Jane Russell?

9

Who was the US commander at the Battle of Cassino?

10

Which oil company was founded by John D Rockefeller?

11

Which former spy revealed some though not all in *My Silent War*?

12

Which French philosopher wrote: "I think therefore I am"?

PEOPLE
WHOSE LAST WORDS WERE THESE?

. . . .

1

"All my possessions for a moment of time."

2

"I should never have switched from scotch to martinis."

3

"Get my swan costume ready."

4

"Rosebud."

5

"God will pardon me, it is His trade."

6

"Good little woman."

7

"I am still alive."

8

"How were the receipts today at Madison Square Gardens?"

9

"Die, my dear doctor? That's the last thing I shall do."

10

"I shall hear in heaven."

11

"That was a great game of golf, fellas."

12

"The rest is silence."

PEOPLE
HEROES AND HEROINES

1

Whose famous victory is remembered on 21 October?

2

Which British nurse did the Germans execute in 1915?

3

Which movie star was one of the USA's most decorated soldiers?

4

Who escaped from Colditz and wrote a book about it?

5

Which holder of the Victoria Cross devoted himself to charity?

6

Which Falklands War recipient of the VC was known as "H"?

7

Who was the founder of the nursing profession?

8

Which World War II heroine did Anna Neagle portray on film?

9

Which island was awarded the George Cross for heroism?

10

Whose "midnight ride" in 1775 alerted the American rebels?

11

Which Scottish king defeated the English at Bannockburn in 1314?

12

Who left saying, "I am just going outside and may be some time"?

PEOPLE
WHICH JOHN?

1

Which John always sang in black?

2

Which John assassinated Abraham Lincoln?

3

Which John's first major film was *A Nightmare on Elm Street*?

4

Which John created Harry "Rabbit" Angstrom?

5

Which John was a famous US chat-show host?

6

Which John signed the Magna Carta?

7

Which John was a leader of the Labour Party?

8

Which John is a classical guitarist?

9

Which John lifted the FA Cup in 2007?

10

Which John won an Oscar for *Ryan's Daughter*?

11

Which John was a celebrated economist?

12

Which John was "public enemy number one"?

1

Which famous lovers poetically eloped in 1846?

2

In which stately home was Winston Churchill born?

3

Which Russian tsar murdered his own son?

4

What does the K stand for in Jerome K Jerome?

5

Who is older, Matt Lucas or David Walliams?

6

Who wrote the Asterix books?

7

Who was brother to the Brontë sisters?

8

What was Princess Anne voted in 1971?

9

A S Byatt is the sister of which other English novelist?

10

Who wrote: "To err is human, to forgive divine"?

11

Russell Brand named his cat after which pop singer?

12

Who is David Mitchell's partner in comedy?

120 PEOPLE
WHO DID THESE BECOME?

1

Joseph Ratzinger

2

William Jefferson Blythe

3

Nguyen Tat Thanh

4

Declan Patrick McManus

5

William Frederick Cody

6

Michael Shalhoub

7

Joseph Vissarionovich Djugashvili

8

Julia Elizabeth Wells

9

K'ung Fu-tzu

10

Martha Jane Cannary

11

William Perks

12

Margaret Hyra

PEOPLE
CRIME ON THEIR MIND

1

Who killed Lee Harvey Oswald?

2

Which Great Train Robber returned from exile in 2001?

3

Who was the "Oklahoma Bomber"?

4

Which spy made a dramatic escape from Wormwood Scrubs in 1966?

5

Who assassinated Martin Luther King?

6

Dr Crippen was arrested at sea through the first use of what?

7

Who was the "Acid Bath Murderer"?

8

For what crime was Al Capone convicted in 1931?

9

Which serial killer lived at 10 Rillington Place?

10

Whose escape from Devil's Island was a film with Steve McQueen?

11

With what creative crime was Tom Keating charged in the 1970s?

12

Who did John Hinckley Jr take a shot at in 1981?

. . . .

1

Chatsworth is the stately home of which ducal family?

2

How is Hearst Castle in California also known?

3

Whose official country residence is Chevening House?

4

Which famous English writer lived at Bateman's?

5

Where is home to the French president?

6

Whose Hollywood mansion was called Pickfair?

7

Which US president's home was Mount Vernon?

8

In which of her homes did Queen Victoria die?

9

Which military duke's home was known as "Number One, London"?

10

Menabilly was which English writer's Cornish home?

11

What is the name of Winston Churchill's former home in Kent?

12

Who was the first prime minister to live at 10 Downing Street?

PEOPLE
ALL SORTS (4)

1

Whose real name was Claude William Dukenfield?

2

Who succeeded William Wordsworth as Poet Laureate?

3

Who was the first American World Chess Champion?

4

In which US city was Raymond Chandler born?

5

Who compiled *The Devil's Dictionary*?

6

Whose name became a generic term for a traitor?

7

Whose 1963 report led to the closure of many UK railway lines?

8

Who were known in the gossip columns as "Ken and Em"?

9

Tomáš Masaryk was the first president of which European country?

10

Which athlete's nickname was "Flo-Jo"?

11

Angelina Jolie's first child was adopted in which country?

12

What was author John Buchan's official title?

PEOPLE
SHOWBIZ SIBLINGS: ADD THE SURNAME

· ·

1

Alec, Stephen and William . . .

· ·

2

Ben and Casey . . .

· ·

3

Babs, Joy and Teddy . . .

· ·

4

Don and Phil . . .

· ·

5

Jake and Maggie . . .

· ·

6

Jonathan and Paul . . .

· ·

7

Eric and Julia . . .

· ·

8

Gary and Martin . . .

· ·

9

Alexis, David, Patricia and Rosanna . . .

· ·

10

Emilio and Renée . . .

· ·

11

Julia and Nadia . . .

· ·

12

Luke and Owen . . .

· ·

125

PEOPLE
WHOSE NICKNAMES?

1

The Bouncing Czech

2

Bloody Mary

3

Louisville Lip

4

Chairman of the Board

5

Hezza

6

The Sex Thimble

7

The Crafty Cockney

8

Billy the Kid

9

The Divine Sarah

10

Bambi

11

The Italian Stallion

12

The Iron Butterfly

1

Which cabinet minister swapped his wife for his secretary in 1997?

2

Who blew the whistle on Monica Lewinsky and Bill Clinton?

3

Which sporting star fathered a child in a broom cupboard?

4

Which UK politician faked his death in Florida in 1974?

5

Which US TV evangelist's fling with a call girl took him off air?

6

Which super model earned 200 hours community service in 2008?

7

Who was the American TV lifestyle guru sent to jail in 2004?

8

Which film star's daughter killed gangster Johnny Stompanato?

9

What undesirable hit list did Burt Reynolds get on to in 2009?

10

What was the name of the gambling club in the Lord Lucan affair?

11

Who was MP Jeremy Thorpe cleared of attempting to murder in 1979?

12

What was Jeffrey Archer found guilty of in 2001?

PEOPLE
ALL SORTS (5)

1

What were the names of the flying Wright Brothers?

2

In which year did the Queen Mother reach her century?

3

Who is the patron saint of lost causes?

4

Who died during the filming of *Gladiator* in 1999?

5

Whose 1950s novel *The Naked Lunch* was initially banned in the US?

6

Which English cartoonist and satirist died in 1996?

7

Which role did Phil Collins play on stage in *Oliver*?

8

Who was on the cover of the first issue of *Playboy* magazine?

9

Which great Austrian composer taught both Mozart and Beethoven?

10

Who was elected president of Poland in 1990?

11

Who wrote a regular newspaper column as the "Wednesday Witch"?

12

Which US president was a former director of the CIA?

PEOPLE
WHO SAID THESE?

1

"They misunderestimated me."

2

"Anyone who says he can see through a woman is missing a lot."

3

"Jaw-jaw is better than war-war."

4

"I'm a Ford, not a Lincoln."

5

"Nothing happened in the sixties except that we all dressed up."

6

"Money is better than poverty, if only for financial reasons."

7

"Politics is too serious a matter to be left to the politicians."

8

"When the President does it, that means that it's not illegal."

9

"I have never delivered a firebrand speech."

10

"For years I thought the club's name was Partick Thistle Nil."

11

"Power is the ultimate aphrodisiac."

12

"As God once said, and I think rightly . . ."

PEOPLE
WHICH SMITH?

1

Which Smith was a show-jumping champion?

2

Which Smith wrote *I Capture the Castle*?

3

Which Smith unilaterally declared Rhodesia's independence?

4

Which Smith was a clergyman, journalist and wit?

5

Which Smith won the men's singles championship at Wimbledon?

6

Which Smith married Pocahontas?

7

Which Smith was an England rugby scrum half?

8

Which Smith wrote the poem "Not Waving but Drowning"?

9

Which Smith is a popular English character actress?

10

Which Smith tailors suits?

11

Which Smith was an 18th-century economist?

12

Which Smith added his weight to the Lib-Dems?

PEOPLE
THE IMMORTALS

1

In Greek mythology, who was enchanted with his own reflection?

2

Which god drove the chariot of the sun across the sky?

3

How many tasks did Hercules have to perform?

4

Who stole fire from Mount Olympus to give to mankind?

5

Which Greek god was known as the "Earthshaker"?

6

Who was the Norse god of thunder?

7

What was the prize in the Judgement of Paris?

8

Who took 20 years to return home from the Trojan War?

9

Who ferried the souls of the dead across the River Styx?

10

Which Egyptian goddess had the head of a cat?

11

Who had the golden touch?

12

Which Greek deity equated with the Roman god Mercury?

PEOPLE
ALL SORTS (6)

1

Whose soul goes marching on?

2

Which celebrated explorer became an MP in 1895?

3

Which famous English writer once clean bowled W G Grace?

4

Who wrote *Confessions of an English Opium-Eater*?

5

Who in the 50s was radio's distinctively voiced "Man in Black"?

6

Kim Basinger's daughter shares the name of which country?

7

Whose rhyming nickname at school was "Bathing Towel"?

8

Which of the play-writing Shaffer twins wrote *Sleuth*?

9

What title did Margaret Thatcher take as a member of the peerage?

10

What is Rupert Murdoch's first name?

11

Who is Tara Newley's famous mother?

12

Who proposed as her epitaph: "Excuse my dust"?

SCIENCE & NATURE
RANDOM SAMPLE (1)

1

To what family do cabbages and cauliflowers belong?

2

What is a beaver's home called?

3

The kiwi uses which sense to hunt for food?

4

What is the medical term for drilling a hole in the skull?

5

Becquerels are a unit of what?

6

Which salad item is *nasturtium officinale*?

7

The word vaccination comes from the Latin name for which animal?

8

What blocks the sun's ultra-violet rays?

9

What animal did the Russians send into space in 1957?

10

What is endocrinology?

11

Mulefoot and Red Wattle are breeds of what animal?

12

Which bird can swim but can't fly?

1

From which plant does belladonna come?

2

What does the herb borage taste like?

3

What is the world's hardest and heaviest wood?

4

What British tree has berries sometimes called "snotty gogs"?

5

What part of a plant produces pollen?

6

How many petals on a wild orchid?

7

What plants have neither flowers nor roots?

8

Californian, Yellow Horned and Opium are types of what?

9

What is the largest seed in the plant kingdom?

10

What plant devours insects?

11

What fungus is used in the production of alcohol?

12

Where do peanut pods ripen?

1

Which garden insect belongs to the locust family?

2

What is the horn of a rhinoceros made from?

3

Where does a "demersal" creature live?

4

Which bear is bigger – brown, grizzly or polar?

5

What kind of feet do palmipeds have?

6

Which animal can be Red, Arctic, Bat-eared and Fennec?

7

What is a badger's home called?

8

Which Australian animal's name means "no drink"?

9

Which is the only bird that can fly backwards?

10

The mule is a cross between what?

11

What are arachnids?

12

A glow-worm is not a worm – what is it?

SCIENCE & NATURE
IDENTIFY THE MISSING COLLECTIVE NAMES

1

A pod of . . .

2

A knot of . . .

3

A farrow of . . .

4

A chatter of . . .

5

An ambush of . . .

6

A tower of . . .

7

A plague of . . .

8

A smack of . . .

9

A clowder of . . .

10

A bouquet of. . .

11

A crash of. . .

12

A tittering of . . .

SCIENCE & NATURE
THE HUMAN BODY

....

1

What is the longest bone in the body?

....

2

Where is the thyroid gland?

....

3

How many chambers does the heart have?

....

4

Where in the body is the labyrinth?

....

5

What are inflamed if you suffer from nephritis?

....

6

How many chromosomes are there in the human body?

....

7

What does REM stand for?

....

8

Who has more ribs, a man or a woman?

....

9

Which hemisphere of the brain controls the left half of the body?

....

10

What is the largest organ in the body?

....

11

What is another name for cartilage?

....

12

Which gland produces insulin?

....

1

Who discovered carbon dioxide in 1754?

2

The redpoll is a member of which family of British birds?

3

What do silkworms feed on?

4

Who was the last man on the moon?

5

What is the world's smallest bird?

6

Acid turns litmus paper which colour?

7

What is carrageen also known as?

8

What was built to test the "Big Bang" theory?

9

What species of mammal is a lemming?

10

Solid carbon dioxide is known by what name?

11

Bronze is a combination of which two metals?

12

The call of which bird resembles human laughter?

SCIENCE & NATURE
WEATHER WISE

1

What does a pluviometer measure?

2

What is the highest cloud formation?

3

What number on the Beaufort Scale denotes a gale?

4

What are the Sirocco and Mistral?

5

What do isobars measure?

6

What is an area of high atmospheric pressure called?

7

The Mercalli Scale is used for measuring what?

8

Where will you find the shipping forecast area of Fastnet?

9

What was the name of the 2005 hurricane that hit New Orleans?

10

Most tornadoes in the Northern Hemisphere spin which way?

11

In which year did the Great Smog engulf London?

12

In folklore, what will be the result of rain on St Swithin's Day?

1

What family of plant is bamboo?

2

Where were satsumas first cultivated?

3

What moss is found in peat bogs?

4

The pohutukawa tree is native to which country?

5

Which part of a flower protects its bud?

6

Polenta flour comes from the seed of which tree?

7

What was the kiwi fruit originally called?

8

How is the Lent Lily better known?

9

What is a puffball?

10

What part of the oak tree is used for tanning leather?

11

What part of a plant catches pollen?

12

On which continent will you find the monkey bread tree?

SCIENCE & NATURE
FURTHER AMONG THE ANIMALS

1

What is the UK's only venomous snake?

2

What is a baby whale called?

3

Which insect performs the Waggle Dance?

4

What species of animal is a porcupine?

5

Which island did the dodo originally inhabit?

6

What is the covering of a deer's antler called?

7

What colour does the male stickleback turn when courting?

8

What animal is a *Canus lupus*?

9

Which animal was domesticated first, the dog or the cat?

10

What is the UK's smallest bat?

11

Which animal's droppings are called spraint?

12

Which water creature shares its name with a Florida river?

SCIENCE & NATURE
RANDOM SAMPLE (3)

1
What is a smolt?

2
What does a BCG vaccination protect you against?

3
Cinnamon and Silver Fox are breeds of which animal?

4
What are Saturn's rings made of?

5
Rickets is caused by a deficiency of which vitamin?

6
What did Wilhelm Röntgen invent?

7
What is the layman's term for nitrous oxide?

8
Heavy water is used in the development of what?

9
In computer terminology, what does HTML stand for?

10
How many pounds are there in 10 kilograms?

11
What is a butterfly pupa called?

12
Which element has the atomic number "1"?

1

What is the world's fastest mammal?

2

What is the world's largest bird of prey?

3

Which dinosaur had the longest tail?

4

What is the world's largest mammal?

5

Which elephant has the biggest ears, African or Indian?

6

Which insect has the shortest life?

7

What is the largest tree fruit in the world?

8

What is the world's slowest mammal?

9

What is the longest snake in the world?

10

What is the world's largest lizard?

11

Which insect is the longest in the world?

12

What is the world's fastest creature?

1

Who is known as "The Father of Medicine"?

2

What is the lay term for infectious mononucleosis?

3

Which disease affects the salivary glands?

4

What is the varicella zoster virus more commonly called?

5

What drug is used to treat malaria?

6

Who carried out the first heart transplant in 1967?

7

In which year was the first test-tube baby delivered?

8

What is Computerised Axial Tomography?

9

What are you having if you suffer a myocardial infarction?

10

What is gypsum also known as?

11

What is an Ishihara Test used for?

12

Which plant produces the heart stimulant digitalis?

1

Name the space telescope launched in 1990.

2

Which is the largest planet in the solar system?

3

What is a supernova?

4

Would a lake on Mars be freezing or boiling?

5

Which comet was highly visible from Earth in 1997?

6

What does the "Bishop's Ring" encircle?

7

Which galaxy is nearest to our own?

8

What is the most abundant element in the universe?

9

How long does it take for sunlight to reach Earth?

10

What planet is often referred to as the Morning Star?

11

Where would you find the "Marsh of Sleep"?

12

What is the Latin name for the Northern Lights?

1

What gives plants their green colour?

2

Hydrophobia is another name for what?

3

How does a digitigrade animal walk?

4

What shaped mark does an adder have on its head?

5

What are Tussock, Burnet and Goat species of?

6

What is 0° Fahrenheit in centigrade?

7

Which gas forms nearly 80% of the earth's atmosphere?

8

Silicon Valley is adjacent to which US city?

9

What does FM stand for in radio?

10

Who became known as "Father of the Atom Bomb"?

11

Scurvy is caused by a deficiency of which vitamin?

12

What was the name of the first cloned sheep?

1

Where is the smallest muscle located?

2

What is the larynx?

3

Which part of the eye contains no blood vessels?

4

What is the average number of hairs on the head?

5

What are the soft spots called on a newborn baby's skull?

6

What is the epidermis?

7

What part of the tongue tastes sweet things?

8

What are the three kinds of teeth (excluding false!)?

9

What is a *latissimus dorsi*?

10

Tinnitus affects which of the senses?

11

What do you actually aggravate when you hit your "funny bone"?

12

What is the hardest material in the human body?

1

Which husband and wife won the Nobel Prize for Physics in 1903?

2

Who defined the law of universal gravitation?

3

Who discovered oxygen in 1774?

4

What did Alexander Fleming discover in 1928?

5

Who wrote *The Interpretation of Dreams*?

6

Who created the first smallpox vaccine?

7

Which great scientist and philosopher was born in Pisa in 1564?

8

Who was the first man to split the atom?

9

Who in 1628 plotted the circulation of blood in the body?

10

Who pioneered the use of antiseptics?

11

What is Albert Einstein best known for?

12

What nationality was the astronomer Nicolaus Copernicus?

1

Ailurophobia

2

Xenophobia

3

Tachophobia

4

Arachnophobia

5

Cyberphobia

6

Gamophobia

7

Apiphobia

8

Hippophobia

9

Hydrophobia

10

Photophobia

11

Ophthalmophobia

12

Phobophobia

1

What is a squirrel's nest called?

2

Which planet's orbit is closest to the sun?

3

What does DVD stand for?

4

The Cephalic Index relates to measuring what part of the body?

5

Where is the home of the Prime Meridian?

6

What is a river otter's nest called?

7

Which element has the highest melting point?

8

Ursine describes which type of animal?

9

Who invented the telegraph code?

10

What is Britain's largest crustacean?

11

In which country was barley first grown?

12

What common British bird is a *Pica pica*?

SCIENCE & NATURE
STRANGE BUT TRUE

1

What is the male honeybee's only role in life?

2

Which insect can jump 130 times its own height?

3

Which sea creature spends its life standing on its head?

4

From what part of Canada do Labrador dogs come?

5

Which fish spends much of its time out of water?

6

Which Hebridean island has wild sheep on it?

7

Which birds never need to drink fresh water?

8

How many eyes do most species of spiders have?

9

Which is the only male creature to give birth?

10

Which common insect has taste buds on its feet?

11

Which sea creature has enough power to illuminate a house?

12

What do queen ants lose after mating?

151

....

1

Whose vision created television?

....

2

What did Tim Berners-Lee invent in 1989?

....

3

Who built the first successful steam locomotive?

....

4

What did Sir Frank Whittle invent in 1928?

....

5

Who in 1835 came up with the revolver?

....

6

What did Sir Christopher Cockerell launch in 1956?

....

7

Who pioneered wireless telegraphy?

....

8

What did Nicolas-Jacques Conté invent in 1795?

....

9

Whose 15th-century invention made this book possible?

....

10

Who invented the bagless vacuum cleaner?

....

11

Whose brainchild was the mercury thermometer?

....

12

What revolutionary camera did Edwin Land invent?

....

SCIENCE & NATURE
WHAT WOULD YOU BE STUDYING?

1

Vulcanology

2

Entomology

3

Podology

4

Seismology

5

Conchology

6

Cetology

7

Otology

8

Palaeoanthropology

9

Nephology

10

Metrology

11

Heliology

12

Ombrology

1

What kind of animal is an opossum?

2

The ohm is a measurement of what?

3

What did Francis Crick and James Watson unravel?

4

What rare birds breed at Loch Garton in Scotland?

5

Which is the brightest star in the night sky?

6

What insect produces "cuckoo spit"?

7

What is a baby hare called?

8

What is the symbol for tin in the periodic table?

9

What medical instrument did Théophile-Hyacinthe Laënnec invent?

10

Which flower's name comes from the French for "lion's tooth"?

11

What vegetable is a *Solanum tuberosum*?

12

What is a "growler"?

1

What does "TT" stand for in the Isle of Man TT Race?

2

Who said: "The bigger they come, the harder they fall"?

3

How many red cards are there in a standard pack?

4

The FIDE is the governing body of which board game?

5

Who was the first man to hit a golf ball on the moon?

6

Which father and son were Formula One world champions?

7

Which English football club is nicknamed "The Posh"?

8

Philippa Roberts was a world champion in which sport?

9

What sporting weapon fires a quarrel?

10

In which year did Cassius Clay become Muhammad Ali?

11

How many lanes has an Olympic-sized swimming pool?

12

What are "zippers" to an American footballer?

SPORTS & GAMES
CRICKET: 1ST INNINGS

1

In which year was *Wisden Cricketers' Almanack* first published?

2

How wide is a regulation cricket pitch?

3

In cricket what name is given to 111 runs?

4

Who was the first wicket-keeper to score 4000 runs in Tests?

5

Which postwar England captain was born in Bangalore?

6

Which ODI trophy do Australia and New Zealand play for?

7

Who was known as the "Master Blaster"?

8

How many first class hundreds did Graham Hick score?

9

In how many ways can a batsman be given out?

10

In which year did Sachin Tendulkar make his Test debut?

11

Where was the original county ground of Essex?

12

How were cricket pitches marked before whitewash?

1

Who was the first professional football player to be knighted?

2

Who are known as the "Socceroos"?

3

When was the Football World Cup first televised?

4

Which English football league club is the most southerly?

5

How is Edson Arantes do Nascimento better known?

6

Who did Zinedine Zidane head butt in the 2006 World Cup final?

7

Which football league club ground is in two countries?

8

Who splashed out and bought Manchester City in 2008?

9

Who did David Beckham follow as a captain of England?

10

What was used in the 1973 FA Cup final for the one and only time?

11

Which Scottish league club is known as "The Doonhamers"?

12

Which shock defeat did England experience in the 1950 World Cup?

1

What are the three main types of golf clubs?

2

What is an "eagle"?

3

British and US women golfers compete for which trophy?

4

What is the diameter of a golf hole?

5

Who was the first left-hander to win a major championship?

6

Which golfer was nicknamed "The Great White Shark"?

7

Who won the 2008 US Masters?

8

In which year did the Ryder Cup begin?

9

Who won her first Women's British Open in 1995?

10

What in golfing parlance is an "ace"?

11

Where is the oldest public golf course in the USA?

12

Which great US golfer died in September 2006?

1

Who won the first Heineken European Cup in 1996?

2

What was rugby league's "Tri-Nations" originally contested as?

3

Which English club is the "Saints"?

4

Which rugby union position does not exist in rugby league?

5

Who was the victorious captain in the 2007 World Cup Final?

6

Who were the last winners of the Five Nations?

7

Whose home ground is the Liberty Stadium?

8

Which two teams compete for the Bowring Bowl?

9

Who led the British Lions to victory in New Zealand in 1971?

10

Who won the 2009 Super 14 final?

11

What is the Calcutta Cup made from?

12

Which French captain became an internationally renowned sculptor?

SPORTS & GAMES
SPORTING CHANCE (2)

1

What is the maximum break in a game of snooker?

2

Who was "Pistol Pete"?

3

Who captained the US Ryder Cup team in 2006?

4

Who was the first World Chess Champion?

5

When a judo referee says *hajime* what does it mean?

6

Complete this US football team's name: Dallas . . .

7

Where did ice hockey originate?

8

How many players in a netball team?

9

Who is the film *Somebody Up There Likes Me* about?

10

Which sport was founded in Britain in 1895?

11

What sport takes place in a velodrome?

12

Name the 2006 BBC Sports Personality of the Year?

1

In which year did Jenson Button win his first Grand Prix?

2

Where was Ayrton Senna killed in 1994?

3

Who was the first Formula One world champion?

4

During a race, what does a blue flag indicate to a driver?

5

What nationality was racing driver Emerson Fittipaldi?

6

"Brain fade" is motor-racing slang for what?

7

Which race lasts for 24 hours?

8

What is the Italian Grand Prix circuit?

9

Who posthumously won the F1 World Championship in 1970?

10

Which French driver had a career total of 51 Grand Prix wins?

11

How did motor racing driver Graham Hill die?

12

Which Formula One team shared the name of a sacred flower?

. . . .

1

What is Andy Murray's tennis-playing brother's name?

2

What is the regulation height of a tennis net at the centre?

3

How many singles titles did Martina Navratilova win?

4

Which tennis star was stabbed on court in 1993?

5

Complete the duo – Newcombe and . . .

6

What is the third Grand Slam event of the year?

7

Why was "Gorgeous Gussie" Moran so called?

8

Who was unseeded when he won his first Wimbledon singles title?

9

Which tennis player did Chris Evert marry in 1979?

10

Which country won the Davis Cup in 2008?

11

Under which name did Billie Jean King first play?

12

Which Brit won the Girls' Singles Title at Wimbledon in 2008?

1

What do the five Olympic rings represent?

2

In which year did London host its first Olympic Games?

3

Who was stripped of his gold medal at the Seoul Olympics?

4

How long is an Olympic marathon (to the nearest mile/kilometre)?

5

How many Olympic gold medals did Tarzan win?

6

Why did several countries boycott the 1956 Olympics?

7

At which Olympics did Steve Redgrave win his first gold medal?

8

Who won gold medals for both the 800m and 1500m at Tokyo in 1964?

9

Which gymnast uniquely achieved a perfect score twice in 1976?

10

In which year did Cassius Clay win an Olympic gold?

11

Who was known as "The Flying Housewife"?

12

What was Team Britain's gold medal tally at Beijing?

SPORTS & GAMES
SPORTING CHANCE (3)

1

Whose nickname was "The Juice"?

2

Who was rugby league's 2008 Man of Steel?

3

What is the inside diameter of a basketball hoop?

4

What sport did Dr James Naismith found in 1891?

5

How many oars are used in sculling?

6

What racing track is rebuilt every year?

7

How long did the 1981 US baseball strike last?

8

What material is used to make a sumo wrestling ring?

9

Which is the world's oldest golf club?

10

What is the alternative name for a castle in chess?

11

When was Lance Armstrong's first win in the Tour de France?

12

Whose ear did Mike Tyson notoriously bite?

SPORTS & GAMES
WHOSE NICKNAMES ARE THESE?

1

Banger

2

Gentleman Jim

3

The Big Easy

4

Little Mo

5

Jukebox

6

Brockett

7

Bumface

8

Boom Boom

9

Smokin' Joe

10

Chariots

11

Zulu

12

Essex Exocet

1

Who was the first international cricket match between?

2

Which Test cricketer was knighted in 1990?

3

In which country is the Pura Cup competition?

4

How old was Ian Botham when Geoffrey Boycott made his Test debut?

5

W G Grace represented England at which other sport?

6

What was The Oval before it became a cricket ground in 1845?

7

Who was "Player of the Tournament" in the 2007 World Cup?

8

Who became president of the MCC in 2008?

9

Who scored the most Test runs – Weekes, Worrell or Walcott?

10

What bird is on the Sussex badge, and how many of them are there?

11

Name England's four captains in the series v West Indies in 1988.

12

Which 19th-century English poet got a black eye from a cricket ball?

1

Who resigned as Celtic manager in May 2009?

2

How many England caps did goalkeeper Peter Shilton win?

3

Who described whom as a "prophet for the 21st-century"?

4

Who scored the only goal in the 2007 FA Cup final?

5

What did Thames Ironworks FC change its name to in 1900?

6

Manager Arsène Wenger has university degrees in which subjects?

7

Which former German POW became a British hero?

8

Who was Cristiano Ronaldo named after?

9

Who did Manchester United pay £29.1m for in 2002?

10

Which international player was known as *Der Kaiser*?

11

Which was the first club to float on the London Stock Exchange?

12

Who was the first goalie to save a penalty in an FA Cup final?

SPORTS & GAMES
SPORTING CHANCE (4)

1

What is the only Test cricket ground below sea level?

2

What is the start of a hockey match called?

3

Which US jockey was called "The Kentucky Kid"?

4

How many Grand Nationals did Red Rum run?

5

Complete this US football team's name: St Louis . . .

6

How many times did Joe Frazier fight Muhammad Ali?

7

Where were the 2006 Commonwealth Games held?

8

Who was Somerset's Australian cricket captain in 2008?

9

In speedway, how many laps are there in a heat?

10

In which sport would you need a foil or an *épée*?

11

For which league football club did Des O'Connor play?

12

Which famous All Black was sent off at Murrayfield in 1967?

SPORT & GAMES
GOLF: 2ND ROUND

1

Where is the home of the Royal and Ancient Golf Club?

2

What do winners of the US Masters get to wear?

3

What is the maximum number of clubs allowed in a bag?

4

Who was the golf professional father of Peter Alliss?

5

In which year did Team Europe first contest the Ryder Cup?

6

What is the term for going three under par on a hole?

7

Who was the first golfer to win $1m in prize money?

8

Which American cricket club has been the venue for the US Open?

9

Who captained Team Europe in the 2008 Ryder Cup?

10

Which golfer's knighthood was announced after his death in 1987?

11

Who became the first Irishman to win The Open for 60 years?

12

In which country is the World Ice Golf Championship held?

1

What tournament is played for the Melrose Cup?

2

Which was the first Welsh club to celebrate its centenary?

3

What are the names of England's Armitage brothers?

4

Who were the first Olympic rugby champions?

5

Who won the first rugby league World Cup in 1954?

6

Who made a topless appearance at Twickenham in 1982?

7

What is the hooker called in French?

8

How many times did Stuart Barnes play for England?

9

Who moved from Llanelli to Widnes in 1988?

10

Which French player won 118 Test caps?

11

What was unique about the 1973 Five Nations?

12

Who in 1996 were rugby league's first Super League champions?

1

Moving clockwise on a dartboard, what number is next to 1?

2

Where did snooker originate?

3

Name the odd one out: king, queen, bishop, cardinal?

4

In which card game can you score "one for his nob"?

5

How many squares on a standard draughts board?

6

In which card game does Omar Sharif excel?

7

Which game takes its name from the Chinese for "sparrow"?

8

In poker, what hand beats a straight flush?

9

Which card game is based on the stock market?

10

What is a grand slam in bridge?

11

In snooker, which colour ball is worth six points?

12

In which game is there a "Doubling Cube"?

SPORTS & GAMES
SPORTING CHANCE (5)

1

Who compete for rugby's Calcutta Cup?

2

In which sport would you see a Fosbury Flop?

3

How many times did Jackie Stewart win the F1 World Championship?

4

In what year was the first Tour de France cycle race?

5

In swimming, what is the trudgen?

6

Who hosted the first Football World Cup in 1930?

7

Who were the two athletic heroes of *Chariots of Fire*?

8

What is rolled in the Canadian sport of birling?

9

What is a Boston crab?

10

When was the first Oxford v Cambridge Boat Race?

11

Who won seven gold medals at the 1972 Olympics?

12

Where was the game of squash invented?

1

Which rugby league side is at home at the JJB Stadium?

2

At which racecourse is the *Prix de l'Arc de Triomphe* run?

3

What is Brazil's most famous football stadium?

4

Where is the cricket Test ground of McLean Park?

5

Where in London were the 1948 Olympics staged?

6

What was Manchester United's ground before Old Trafford?

7

Where was the Muhammad Ali-George Foreman rumble in the jungle?

8

What baseball stadium is home to the Chicago Cubs?

9

What sport is played at Valderrama?

10

What Test cricket ground is reduced to "The Gabba"?

11

Where is the San Siro Stadium?

12

What was the world's first purpose-built motor-racing circuit?

1

Who uniquely won world championships on both two and four wheels?

2

What nationality was racing driver Jody Scheckter?

3

Which 1950s British racing driver had a withered arm?

4

To whose career is a museum at Duns in Scotland dedicated?

5

What did the Formula One team Elf-Tyrrell introduce in 1976?

6

Who was the first Briton to win the F1 World Championship?

7

Who became the first driver to win six times in a row at Le Mans?

8

What in 2009 was declared the new home of the British Grand Prix?

9

Which British driver won the F1 World Championship in 1976?

10

Which US race takes place annually over Memorial Day weekend?

11

Which was Michael Schumacher's first Formula One winning team?

12

Who became president of the FIA in 1993?

1

Who is the tallest of the Williams sisters, Venus or Serena?

2

Who was the first black player to win a Wimbledon singles title?

3

Which female player won a gold medal at the 1988 Seoul Olympics?

4

What is the venue for the US Open?

5

Which future English monarch played at Wimbledon in 1926?

6

Who is the only player to have achieved two calendar Grand Slams?

7

Who was the first player to serve over 1000 aces in a season?

8

Which Australian tennis star became Mrs Roger Cawley?

9

Who did Roger Federer beat in his first Wimbledon final?

10

Who became the youngest-ever US Open champion in 1979?

11

Which US tennis star of the 1920s died in poverty in 1953?

12

What nationality is Marcos Baghdatis?

SPORTS & GAMES

BROTHERS IN SPORT: ADD THE SURNAMES

1

Rory and Tony . . .

2

Irfan and Yusuf . . .

3

John and Justin . . .

4

Graeme and Peter . . .

5

Gavin and Scott . . .

6

Michael and Ralf . . .

7

Gary and Phil . . .

8

Adam and Ben . . .

9

David and John . . .

10

Juan Martin Fernandez and Ignacio Fernandez . . .

11

Henry and Jim . . .

12

Frank and Ronald . . .

SPORTS & GAMES
SPORTING CHANCE (6)

1

What is the longest-running trophy in international sport?

2

What was Nigel Mansell's unique double in 1992-93?

3

Which female athlete was famous for running barefoot?

4

Which Czech Wimbledon champion represented Egypt?

5

What is an oxer?

6

Who won the first Rugby Union World Cup in 1987?

7

Where did the game pelota originate?

8

In which year did ice skater Robin Cousins win an Olympic gold?

9

Which 1963 movie was set in the world of rugby league?

10

What sport is divided into chukkas?

11

How many times did Ryan Sidebottom's father play for England?

12

Andy Farrell's first rugby union Test try was against whom?

1

What does ECG stand for?

2

What is known as the "King of the Spey"?

3

Which nation first gave women the right to vote?

4

What is the next prime number after 71?

5

How many letters are there in the modern Welsh alphabet?

6

Where were the Bee Gees born?

7

Which household item is made from naphthalene?

8

What is the most common non-contagious disease?

9

Which liqueur is used in a Sidecar cocktail?

10

Which instrument did Lionel Hampton play?

11

Who led the Peasants' Revolt of 1381?

12

What was London's first one-way street?

1

What was once called brimstone?

2

How many sides are there in a pair of nonagons?

3

Who was Peeping Tom peeping at?

4

What colour is carmine?

5

What is the art of shaping hedges called?

6

Love Apple is an old-fashioned name for what?

7

What does *Götterdämmerung* mean?

8

Ben Lomond and Baldwin are types of which fruit?

9

On which geological fault line is San Francisco?

10

What are Moss, Garter and Cable types of?

11

Which famous cat was created by Otto Messmer?

12

What did Jerry's Guide to the World Wide Web become?

1

To which flower family does garlic belong?

2

In which country was the Bayeux Tapestry embroidered?

3

What relation is Liza Minnelli to Lorna Luft?

4

What is "The Old Lady of Threadneedle Street"?

5

What trees can grow above the tree line?

6

Who designed a seaplane called "The Spruce Goose"?

7

Who is the patron saint of Glasgow?

8

What was the name of Gene Autry's horse?

9

What does MCC add up to in roman numerals?

10

Which playwright became his country's president in 1989?

11

Name the winged horse in Greek mythology.

12

Who is Cleo Laine's bandleader husband?

GENERAL KNOWLEDGE
NUMBER 4

1

Which butterfly has the same name as a punctuation mark?

2

What is the capital of Uzbekistan?

3

For how many years was Robinson Crusoe marooned?

4

Which Netherlands city is famous for its porcelain?

5

Name the three wise men of the Nativity story.

6

What is Miss Piggy's surname?

7

On which racecourse is the Scottish Grand National run?

8

In which sport was Molly Hide an England star performer?

9

Eboracum is the Roman name for which English city?

10

What is campanology?

11

What is the calendar used by most Western nations?

12

What does the Japanese word *kamikaze* mean?

1

Who was New Zealand's first woman prime minister?

2

What is the chemical symbol for potassium?

3

Which girl's name means "my father rejoices"?

4

What is dactylology?

5

Which English king had the nickname "Tum-Tum"?

6

Which language has the most native speakers?

7

Which Mecca of alternative comedy opened in London in 1979?

8

What is the name of the Obama family dog acquired in 2009?

9

Which racecourse is home to the St Leger?

10

Who designed the Clifton Suspension Bridge?

11

What does Volkswagen mean?

12

What do the Four Horsemen of the Apocalypse represent?

1

How many books are there in the New Testament?

2

Which grow upwards, stalactites or stalagmites?

3

In which ocean is the Gulf Stream?

4

Who was the manager of the Sex Pistols?

5

Which famous riding school is in Vienna?

6

What did the Pope become in 1870?

7

A Turk's Head is a type of what?

8

In which year did UK National Service end?

9

Who designed the Morris Minor?

10

What is a gallivat?

11

In darts slang, what score is "bed and breakfast"?

12

Which English writer won the Nobel Prize for Literature in 1932?

GENERAL KNOWLEDGE
NUMBER 7

1

What does VSOP stand for on a bottle of brandy?

2

Which England soccer player was the Charlton brothers' uncle?

3

How is Lesley Hornby better known?

4

In heraldry, what colour is sable?

5

What is the collective noun for kangaroos?

6

Who invented the lightning conductor?

7

In rugby, which two countries play for the Dave Gallagher Cup?

8

Who composed the *March Slav*?

9

Which German spa gave its name to an item of men's headwear?

10

Which 60s pop duo changed their name from Tom and Jerry?

11

In Morse code, what letter is represented by four dots?

12

How many biblical plagues of Egypt were there?

1

Name the six annual Nobel Prize categories.

2

What do "almost" and "biopsy" have in common?

3

What brand was the subject of the first-ever TV advert in the UK?

4

Which of the Seven Wonders of the World was at Olympia?

5

Which artist painted his *Bedroom in Arles*?

6

Who was the South African prime minister assassinated in 1966?

7

What is the symbol of the World Wildlife Fund?

8

Which Russian novelist wrote *The Government Inspector*?

9

What do the initials FLAG stand for?

10

What is the knife carried by Gurkha soldiers called?

11

Who had a 1950s hit with "Dream Lover"?

12

Who is the patron saint of taxi drivers?

1

What was Dr Josef Mengele called?

2

Who succeeded Bobby Robson as England's football manager?

3

The island of Zanzibar is part of which country?

4

What does a notaphile collect?

5

Which English explorer was killed in Hawaii in 1779?

6

Who was the child with the magic talking piano?

7

What is usually kept in a bandbox?

8

Split Waterman captained England in what sport?

9

Who had a 1980s hit with "Stand And Deliver"?

10

Who are Huey, Dewey and Louie?

11

On which day of the week did Solomon Grundy marry?

12

In Hawaiian, does *aloha* mean hello or goodbye?

1

Where did the game of Fives originate?

2

How many times were Torvill and Dean World Ice Dance Champions?

3

Who created the Cornish detective Wycliffe?

4

What is a "Beauty of Bath"?

5

In which country were Venetian blinds invented?

6

The mythological centaur is part man and part what?

7

What is Spider-Man's real name?

8

Whose military defences were called the Maginot Line?

9

What was known as the "Tin Lizzie"?

10

Which letter is to the right of B on a computer keyboard?

11

What is etymology?

12

What is the Jewish Day of Atonement also called?

1

How many psalms are there in the Book of Psalms?

2

In the shipping forecast, which area is east of Tyne?

3

Who was the Enlightened One?

4

If you are crapulous what are you?

5

Al Gore was the US senator for which state?

6

Who narrated Jeff Wayne's "The War of the Worlds"?

7

In which English city was Guy Fawkes born?

8

For which two English cricket counties did Chris Broad play?

9

Name the eight countries that border France.

10

What can be a short jacket or a dance?

11

What is the cube root of 64?

12

In which country is the football team Anderlecht?

GENERAL KNOWLEDGE
NUMBER 12

1

Who said: "There's a sucker born every minute"?

2

What is a moke?

3

Who sends encyclical letters?

4

Who in 1848 wrote *The Communist Manifesto*?

5

What was the last league club George Best played for?

6

In which London palace was Queen Elizabeth I born?

7

Who wrote the theme music for the film *Kill Bill*?

8

Where in California is Disneyland?

9

What is a natterjack?

10

In the Bible, who first saw the writing on the wall?

11

What is *pâté de foie gras*?

12

What does a necrologist write?

GENERAL KNOWLEDGE
NUMBER 13

1

What is pinchbeck?

2

Who said: "An army marches on its stomach"?

3

What animal does a *mahout* take care of?

4

How did Otis Reading die?

5

What is examined using an otoscope?

6

What is one third of one half?

7

Who wrote the novel *White Teeth*?

8

Which English player won the Women's Singles at Wimbledon in 1969?

9

Parmentier means garnished or cooked with which vegetable?

10

Who composed the opera *Peter Grimes*?

11

Who is the younger Attenborough, David or Richard?

12

Tony Curtis said of which co-star: "It was like kissing Hitler"?

1

Alphabetically, what is the first creature in the dictionary?

2

By what two other names has St Petersburg been known?

3

At sea, how long is a dogwatch?

4

Which group of islands includes St Martin's and Tresco?

5

What did Anton Drexler found in 1919?

6

In which city are cricket Tests played at the Wankhede Stadium?

7

What does the Q stand for in IQ?

8

Which England goalkeeper was nicknamed "The Cat"?

9

What is the last letter of the modern Greek alphabet?

10

Who were Buster's Diaries told to?

11

Which number is the current French Republic?

12

In which sport might you do a Triffus?

1

Which country's currency is the dalasi?

2

Which Disney film features the song "Topsy Turvy"?

3

In which city does the annual Oktoberfest take place?

4

Which is the sixth of the Ten Commandments?

5

How many pecks are there in a bushel?

6

They may be complex, vulgar or mixed – what are they?

7

What was U2's first album?

8

What French town gave the bayonet its name?

9

Who played Inspector Craddock in four *Miss Marple* films?

10

Where in Paris is the tomb of Napoleon?

11

What do the initials stand for in P D James?

12

What is the French stock exchange called?

1

"The Glovers" is the nickname of which English league football team?

2

Which Salman Rushdie novel won the 1981 Booker Prize?

3

In which London surburb was Charlie Chaplin born?

4

In Ireland, what is the prime minister called?

5

What word both means halo and cloud?

6

Who played Irene in the 1960s TV series *The Forsyte Saga*?

7

What colour is the "black box" on an aircraft?

8

What was Greta Garbo's real name?

9

What is the name of the bobsleigh course at St Moritz?

10

Who wrote the Elizabethan play *The Spanish Tragedy*?

11

What speed limit was introduced on British roads in 1965?

12

Ikebana is the Japanese art of what?

GENERAL KNOWLEDGE
NUMBER 17

1

In which US state is the Painted Desert?

2

Whose motto is "Nation Shall Speak Peace Unto Nation"?

3

What is the principal ingredient in the Indian dish dahl?

4

Under which pen name did C Day-Lewis write detective novels?

5

Who was the great Athenian sculptor of the 5th century?

6

Name the character played by Mickey Rourke in *The Wrestler*.

7

Who captained the 1974 British Lions in South Africa?

8

MP Dennis Skinner is known as "The Beast" of where?

9

What part of an animal's body is its carapace?

10

Who created the TV sitcom *The Thin Blue Line*?

11

How many strings does a balalaika have?

12

In *The Archers*, where do Nigel and Elizabeth Pargetter live?

1

Which literary family lived at Haworth in Yorkshire?

2

Who did Edward Heath succeed as Conservative Party leader?

3

Which father and daughter starred in the film *Tiger Bay*?

4

What is the motto on the Prince of Wales's feathers?

5

In the Bible, who was King Ahab married to?

6

Which poet was a member of Oliver Cromwell's Council of State?

7

In which sport is nose riding a manoeuvre?

8

How many sides does a dodecagon have?

9

Who wrote the anti-war novel *All Quiet on the Western Front*?

10

What is the capital of Vietnam?

11

Who directed the film *The Queen*?

12

Where do mice who are proverbially poor live?

GENERAL KNOWLEDGE
NUMBER 19

1

What was the Roman name for the city of Bath?

2

What item of headgear first appeared in London in 1797?

3

Who won the most England caps, Bobby Charlton or Billy Wright?

4

Where is Charles Darwin buried?

5

Which tradesman would use a quern?

6

Who wrote *The Legend of Sleepy Hollow*?

7

Whose motto was "All for one, one for all"?

8

At which two sports did Rachel Heyhoe Flint represent England?

9

Who did the Germans call *Der Bingle*?

10

Francis Chichester sailed around the world in which boat?

11

What was the name of the dog on the HMV label?

12

Dove Cottage was the home of which English poet?

1

Who played the title role in the film *Hans Christian Andersen*?

2

What do you call whipped cream flavoured with vanilla?

3

Which flag is flown when a ship is about to sail?

4

What is the centre of an atom called?

5

In which year did the IRA come into being?

6

What is the family's surname in Louisa May Alcott's *Little Women*?

7

What side of a ship is starboard, left or right?

8

Which English operatic festival was founded in 1934?

9

How many hours are there in a fortnight?

10

In curling, the tee sits in the centre of what?

11

Which English novelist won the Nobel Prize in 2007?

12

Who composed the music for *A Chorus Line*?

GENERAL KNOWLEDGE
NUMBER 21

1

What was Richard Burton's last film?

2

How is the German Ardennes offensive of 1944 better known?

3

Which prima ballerina married a Panamanian diplomat in 1955?

4

What are Norway lobsters called when cooked?

5

What rope is used for tying up a ship?

6

Which crab makes its home in another creature's shell?

7

In Greek mythology, which trio represented beauty?

8

Who is the patron saint of Venice?

9

Which England football manager did Terry Venables succeed?

10

Who plays Madonna's chauffeur in the video of her song "Music"?

11

Which US vice-president couldn't spell "potato"?

12

Who invented the miners' safety lamp?

GENERAL KNOWLEDGE
NUMBER 22

1

Whose motto is *Per ardua ad astra*?

2

Which Charles created the comic strip *Peanuts*?

3

Who was the Egyptian sun god?

4

In which castle on the Isle of Wight was Charles I imprisoned?

5

Manama is the capital of which Middle Eastern country?

6

Who was the leading poet of the Beat Movement?

7

Who composed "The Dam Busters March"?

8

What colour is a ship's quarantine flag?

9

Who presented the TV arts series *Monitor*?

10

Which is the world's oldest existing city?

11

What do ichthyologists study?

12

In which Charles Dickens novel is Mrs Pardiggle a character?

1

Which religious movement did Mary Baker Eddy found?

2

Which barrel is larger, a butt or a hogshead?

3

Which expression did style guru Peter York coin in 1975?

4

What are "spring" and "neap" types of?

5

Who composed music for both the 1937 and 1953 Coronations?

6

What was the first bird released from Noah's Ark?

7

Who did Renate Blauel marry on Valentine's Day, 1984?

8

On what date in 1951 was *The Archers* first broadcast nationally?

9

Who wrote *The Decline and Fall of the Roman Empire*?

10

Which 12th-century band of knights protected pilgrims to the Holy Land?

11

What are Gold Murderer and Thunder & Lightning?

12

When was the first-ever London Marathon?

1

What is a liana?

2

What is the last book in the New Testament?

3

How is the former Viscount Stansgate better known?

4

Which art movement did Pablo Picasso and Georges Braque begin?

5

What are the top universities in the US known as?

6

Which is greater, 2/3rd or 7/10th?

7

Whose address was 23 Railway Cuttings, East Cheam?

8

Who played the title role in *The Life and Death of Peter Sellers*?

9

What does MG stand for in the well-known make of car?

10

In which sport would you wear an obi?

11

Which poet's ashes were buried at East Coker in Somerset?

12

In its original French, what does the word biscuit mean?

ANSWERS
ART & LITERATURE

. . . .

WORDS AND PICTURES (1)

. . . .

1. Charlotte; 2. Michelangelo; 3. Captain Nemo; 4. Andy Goldsworthy;
5. *The White Tiger;* 6. Polish; 7. The Louvre in Paris;
8. *The Return of the King*; 9. Terry Pratchett; 10. Joanne Kathleen;
11. *Casino Royale*; 12. 18th

CHILDREN'S BOOKS

. . . .

1. Timmy; 2. John Tenniel; 3. John Ridd; 4. *Harry Potter and the
Prisoner of Azkaban*; 5. Rudyard Kipling; 6. Michael and John;
7. Big Friendly Giant; 8. L Frank Baum; 9. Wilbur the pig;
10. Flopsy, Mopsy, Cottontail;
11. *The Little Prince;* 12. Jacob and Wilhelm

MODERN ART

. . . .

1. Jackson Pollock; 2. Cubism; 3. Guernica; 4. Andy Warhol;
5. Peter Blake; 6. The Stars and Stripes; 7. Edward Hopper;
8. Lucian Freud; 9. Sidney Nolan; 10. Ireland; 11. Bridget Riley;
12. Salvador Dali

POETS AND POETRY

. . . .

1. Westminster Abbey; 2. Samuel Taylor Coleridge;
3. Carol Ann Duffy; 4. Paradise; 5. Four; 6. Robert Burns';
7. Wystan Hugh; 8. Sylvia Plath's; 9. Nightingale; 10. John Donne;
11. Bysshe; 12. John Betjeman

ANSWERS
ART & LITERATURE

FAMOUS PEN NAMES

1. Lewis Carroll; 2. John le Carré; 3. Mark Twain; 4. Fay Weldon;
5. Voltaire; 6. Agatha Christie; 7. O Henry; 8. George Orwell;
9. George Eliot; 10. Isak Dinesen; 11. Ellis Bell; 12. Ellery Queen

WORDS AND PICTURES (2)

1. John Steinbeck; 2. Camille Pissarro; 3. Alarm clock;
4. Graham Sutherland's; 5. Michael Crichton; 6. Pablo Picasso's;
7. "Daffodils" by William Wordsworth; 8. Bilbo Baggins;
9. Douglas Adams; 10. Raffaello Santi; 11. George Gissing;
12. Auguste Rodin

THE WORLD OF CHARLES DICKENS

1. Portsmouth; 2. *The Mystery of Edwin Drood*; 3. *David Copperfield*;
4. Jack Dawkins; 5. Ellen Ternan; 6. London and Paris;
7. Sarah Gamp; 8. *Hard Times*; 9. Jacob Marley;
10. Marshalsea prison; 11. Wackford Squeers; 12. *Barnaby Rudge*

WHO PAINTED THESE?

1. Thomas Gainsborough; 2. Jan Vermeer; 3. John Constable;
4. Pieter Bruegel the Elder; 5. Gustav Klimt; 6. Leonardo da Vinci;
7. Edvard Munch; 8. Théodore Géricault; 9. Frans Hals;
10. Vincent van Gogh; 11. Hieronymus Bosch; Sir Edwin Landseer

ANSWERS
ART & LITERATURE

CLASSIC CHARACTERS

1. Athos, Porthos, Aramis; 2. Michael Henchard; 3. *Moby Dick;*
4. Emma; 5. *Sense and Sensibility*; 6. Sherlock Holmes;
7. Becky Sharp; 8. Rosinante; 9. *Crime and Punishment*;
10. Lemuel; 11. Raffles; 12. Uncas

LITERARY SLEUTHS

1. Dorothy L Sayers; 2. *The Big Sleep*; 3. Sherlock Holmes;
4. Nancy Drew; 5. C Auguste Dupin; 6. Father Brown;
7. Mike Hammer; 8. Australia; 9. Jules; 10. Dashiell Hammett;
11. Ngaio Marsh; 12. William of Baskerville

WORDS AND PICTURES (3)

1. *Prix Goncourt*; 2. Madrid; 3. Canadian; 4. Casanova;
5. John Buchan's; 6. Charles Kingsley; 7. A maquette;
8. Ezra Pound; 9. Mural; 10. *Sense and Sensibility*;
11. Barbara Cartland's; 12. John James Audubon

NUMBERS GAME

1. Ken Kesey; 2. Wolf Mankowitz; 3. Jerome K Jerome;
4. Frederick Forsyth; 5. Edith Nesbit; 6. A A Milne; 7. T E Lawrence;
8. Alistair MacLean; 9. Anne Fine; 10. Agatha Christie;
11. Donald Harstad; 12. William Shakespeare

ANSWERS
ART & LITERATURE

....

ARTISTS IN THE FRAME
....

1. Joshua Reynolds; 2. (Sandro) Botticelli's; 3. Claude Monet;
4. Paul Gauguin; 5. Russia; 6. Michelangelo Caravaggio;
7. Laura Knight; 8. Laurence Stephen; 9. The horse;
10. Peter Paul Rubens; 11. El Greco; 12. James McNeill Whistler

....

ALL ABOUT THE BARD
....

1. Anne Hathaway; 2. Julius Caesar; 3. *The Taming of the Shrew*;
4. Trojan War; 5. *The Winter's Tale*; 6. Montague and Capulet;
7. *The Tempest*; 8. *Timon of Athens*; 9. St George's (23 April);
10. Forest of Arden; 11. Goneril, Regan, Cordelia; 12. Lucrece

....

WORDS AND PICTURES (4)
....

1. Nick Hornby's; 2. Sir Edwin Landseer; 3. Wigan Pier; 4. Three;
5. Dadaism; 6. Father; 7. F A Bartholdi;
8. Elizabeth, Jane, Mary, Lydia, Kitty; 9. Prehistoric cave paintings;
10. Captain Ahab; 11. Van Dyck (later Sir Anthony Vandyke);
12. Leo Tolstoy

....

MORE POETS AND POETRY
....

1. Henry Wadsworth Longfellow; 2. John Masefield;
3. Thomas Stearns; 4. 14; 5. Roger McGough; 6. Seamus Heaney's;
7. William Wordsworth; 8. "Funeral Blues"; 9. Thomas Chatterton;
10. George; 11. Federico García Lorca; 12. Wendy Cope

....

ANSWERS
ART & LITERATURE

PLAYS AND PLAYWRIGHTS

1. Harold Pinter; 2. T S Eliot; 3. Peter Shaffer's; 4. *Pygmalion*;
5. *A Streetcar Named Desire*; 6. Sophocles; 7. Czechoslovakia;
8. Christopher Marlowe; 9. *The Vagina Monologues*;
10. George Bernard Shaw; 11. *The Crucible*; 12. Brendan Behan

OLD MASTERS

1. Venice; 2. Goya; 3. Claude Monet; 4. Eight; 5. *Diana and Actaeon*;
6. Henri de Toulouse-Lautrec's; 7. Edouard Manet; 8. Hans Holbein's;
9. Edgar Degas; 10. John Everett Millais; 11. J M W Turner;
12. Jacques Louis David

FICTIONAL PLACES

1. Narnia; 2. Thomas Hardy's; 3. *Gulliver's Travels*; 4. Airstrip One;
5. Hobbits; 6. William Faulkner; 7. Peter Pan; 8. Anthony Trollope;
9. Garrison Keillor's; 10. *Lost Horizon*; 11. Maple White Land;
12. *Under Milk Wood*

20TH-CENTURY CLASSICS

1. Richard Adams; 2. *Rebecca* (Daphne du Maurier);
3. Mellors the gamekeeper; 4. Gunther Grass; 5. Humbert Humbert;
6. *Scoop*; 7. *Animal Farm*; 8. Paul Scott; 9. *Catcher in the Rye*;
10. *For Whom the Bell Tolls*; 11. *A Clockwork Orange*; 12. Harper Lee's

ANSWERS
ART & LITERATURE

MORE MODERN ART

1. Damien Hirst's; 2. Antony Gormley; 3. 2000; 4. Mark Rothko;
5. Tracey Emin's; 6. Charles Saatchi; 7. Belgian; 8. Mark Wallinger's;
9. Flowers; 10. Yorkshire; 11. Roy Lichtenstein;
12. Gilbert and George

MORE CHILDREN'S BOOKS

1. Alice in *Alice in Wonderland*; 2. Ted Hughes; 3. Bear;
4. Nancy and Peggy; 5. Psamead (sand fairy); 6. Pew;
7. *Madame Doubtfire*; 8. Captain Frederick Marryat; 9. Veruca Salt;
10. Chimney-sweep; 11. Dr Doolittle; 12. *The Amber Spyglass*

WORDS AND PICTURES (5)

1. Henry James; 2. St Ives; 3. South Africa; 4. Sir Walter Scott;
5. Banksy; 6. London magistrate; 7. Arnold Bennett's; 8. Bilbao;
9. *Carrie:* 10. The Turkey; 11. Vladimir Nabokov; 12. Rolf Harris

ANSWERS
CINEMA & TELEVISION

. . . .

MOVIE TITLES (1): ADD THE NUMBERS

. . . .

1. *12*; 2. *Three*; 3. *8*; 4. *Two*; 5. *13*; 6. *23*; 7. *Seven*;
8. *Nine*; 9. *92*; 10. *Six*; 11. *Five*; 12. *20,000*

TV SITCOMS

. . . .

1. Walmington-on-Sea; 2. Nanette; 3. HMP Slade; 4. Type For You;
5. Accountant and mailman; 6. St Barnabas; 7. Art and Maths;
8. Miss Gatsby and Miss Tibbs; 9. *All in the Family*;
10. Ferris and Collier; 11. *Last of the Summer Wine*; 12. Gladys Pugh

WHAT ARE THEIR SCREEN NAMES?

. . . .

1. Rock Hudson; 2. Charlton Heston; 3. Rita Hayworth;
4. Boris Karloff; 5. Whoopi Goldberg; 6. Kirk Douglas;
7. Lauren Bacall; 8. Alan Alda; 9. Ben Kingsley; 10. Diana Dors;
11. Cher; 12. Robert Taylor

WESTERN MOVIES

. . . .

1. Kirk Douglas; 2. *The Big Country*: 3. Sam Peckinpah; 4. *Stagecoach*;
5. Nat King Cole and Stubby Kaye; 6. James Stewart;
7. Annie Proulx's; 8. *Guns in the Afternoon*; 9. Steve McQueen;
10. Wyatt Earp; 11. Claudia Cardinale; 12. Marlon Brando

ANSWERS
CINEMA & TELEVISION

···

MULTISCREEN (1)
···

1. William Hartnell; 2. Replicants; 3. *Julia;* 4. Christmas Day (1995);
5. Sue Cook and Nick Ross; 6. *Some Like It Hot*; 7. Donald Sutherland;
8. Rigsby in *Rising Damp*; 9. Byron; 10. Martin Clunes;
11. Daniel Day-Lewis; 12. *8 Mile*

···

TV CRIMEBUSTERS
···

1. Peter Boyd; 2. Sandra Pullman in *New Tricks*; 3. Kojak;
4. St Mary Mead; 5. Paul Michael Glaser and David Soul;
6. *Softly, Softly;* 7. Jersey's Bureau des Etrangers; 8. *Hawaii Five-O*;
9. David Caruso; 10. Samantha Stewart; 11. Judith; 12. DCI Gene Hunt

···

FESTIVALS AND AWARDS
···

1. British Academy of Film and Television Arts; 2. 1928; 3. *True Grit;*
4. Hattie McDaniel (Best Supporting Actress for *Gone with the Wind*,
1939); 5. Golden Lion; 6. Daniel Day-Lewis;
7. George C Scott (for *Patton*); 8. San Sebastian;
9. *Terms of Endearment*; 10. Charles Chaplin (*The Circus*);
11. Robert Redford; 12. *The English Patient*

···

CRIME MOVIES
···

1. Donald Sutherland; 2. Ridley Scott; 3. *Heat*; 4. *Black Rain*;
5. Gwyneth Paltrow; 6. Woody Harrelson; 7. *Gumshoe*;
8. Buster Edwards; 9. Hell; 10. *The Long Goodbye*; 11. J J Gittes;
12. *The Boston Strangler*

···

ANSWERS
CINEMA & TELEVISION

TV SOAPS

1. Los Barcos; 2. Minibus crash; 3. 1986; 4. *Crossroads*;
5. *Home and Away*; 6. Lily Savage and Lloyd Grossman;
7. Mike Reid; 8. Art Malik; 9. *Hollyoaks*;
10. Derek Thompson's (Dee Sadler and Charlie Thompson);
11. Olympic hurdler Colin Jackson; 12. *Soap*

MULTISCREEN (2)

1. Boston; 2. Joel and Ethan; 3. Allison Janney;
4. *Harry Potter and the Order of the Phoenix*; 5. Natasha Kaplinsky;
6. John Osborne; 7. Terry Nation; 8. Peter Jackson; 9. *Pop Idol*;
10. Chris Columbus; 11. Dec (by two months); 12. Cate Blanchett,
Nicole Kidman, Russell Crowe, Geoffrey Rush

JAMES BOND MOVIES

1. *Dr No;* 2. Madonna; 3. They made seven films each;
4. Timothy Dalton; 5. Sean Bean; 6. Australian; 7. His hat;
8. The role of Blofeld; 9. *Never Say Never Again*;
10. Desmond Llewelyn; 11. David Niven; 12. Sean Connery (32)

MOVIE MUSICALS

1. Tim Curry; 2. Sharks and Jets; 3. *The Philadelphia Story;*
4. Glynis Johns; 5. Cy Coleman; 6. Damon Runyon's;
7. *The Barkleys of Broadway*; 8. Jonathan Pryce; 9. Carol Reed;
10. *Singin' in the Rain;* 11. Gene Kelly; 12. John C Reilly

ANSWERS
CINEMA & TELEVISION

TV COOKS

1. Australian; 2. Antony Worrall Thompson's; 3. Graham Kerr;
4. Philip Harben; 5. Ainsley Harriott; 6. A food poisoning scare;
7. Norwich City; 8. Marco Pierre White; 9. Phil Vickery;
10. James Martin; 11. Jamie Oliver; 12. Clarissa Dickson Wright

MOVIE TITLES (2): ADD THE PLACE NAMES

1. *Peking*; 2. *Broadway*; 3. *Alaska*; 4. *Titfield*; 5. *Cairo*; 6. *Bagdad*;
7. *Greenwich*; 8. *Cherbourg*; 9. *Falworth*; 10. *Marienbad*;
11. *Casablanca*; 12. *Tokyo*

CLINT EASTWOOD AND HIS MOVIES

1. .44 Magnum; 2. *Paint Your Wagon;* 3. William Munny;
4. *Play Misty for Me*; 5. *Absolute Power*; 6. Film director John Huston;
7. Rowdy Yates; 8. Mayor of Carmel; 9. James Garner, Donald
Sutherland, Tommy Lee Jones; 10. Sondra Locke;
11. Chief Dan George; 12. Clint Eastwood, Lee Van Cleef, Eli Wallach

MULTISCREEN (3)

1.Virginia Woolf; 2. Ork; 3. Sir Alan Parker;
4. *The Absent-Minded Professor;* 5. Ronnie Corbett and Ronnie Barker;
6. Barney Rubble; 7. James Cromwell; 8. Marion Michael Morrison;
9. Linda Thorson; 10. Mrs Weasley; 11. Charlie Chaplin;
12. Damian Lewis

ANSWERS
CINEMA & TELEVISION

....

ANIMALS ON SCREEN
....

1. Ross in *Friends*; 2. White Persian; 3. Trigger; 4. Toto; 5. 72;
6. The Pie; 7. As Lassie; 8. Keiko the whale; 9. Moose and Enzo;
10. Arthur; 11. German Shepherd; 12. Clyde

....

TV LOCATIONS
....

1. Hastings; 2. Greenwich Village; 3. Portmeirion; 4. *The Office*;
5. Chester; 6. Seattle; 7. Holmfirth; 8. Holland Park; 9. Shropshire;
10. Crimpton-on-Sea; 11. Kenwood House, Hampstead; 12. Dublin

....

FAMILY CONNECTIONS
....

1. Jennifer Saunders; 2. First cousins; 3. Nigel Havers';
4. Janette Scott; 5. Judi Dench and Michael Williams;
6. Jonny Lee Miller; 7. Jack Nicholson; 8. Françoise Dorléac;
9. Herbert Asquith; 10. Margaux and Mariel Hemingway;
11. Keira Knightley; 12. Steve Forrest

....

WHOSE CATCHPHRASES WERE THESE?
....

1. Larry Grayson; 2. Jimmy Durante; 3. Tommy Cooper;
4. Miniature Dennis Waterman (David Walliams) in *Little Britain*;
5. *Rowan & Martin's Laugh-In*; 6. Kojak (Telly Savalas);
7. Ronnie Barker; 8. Little Jim (Peter Sellers) in *The Goon Show*;
9. Dick Emery; 10. Number 6 (Patrick McGoohan) in *The Prisoner*;
11. Tim Nice-But-Dim (Harry Enfield); 12. Edward R Murrow

....

ANSWERS
CINEMA & TELEVISION

....

ALFRED HITCHCOCK MOVIES

....

1. Daphne du Maurier's; 2. Martin Balsam;
3. Charles Laughton and Elsa Lanchester;
4. *The Man Who Knew Too Much;* 5. Photographer; 6. Salvador Dali;
7. *Under Capricorn;* 8. Robert Donat; 9. The Cricket Test score;
10. A baby; 11. Mount Rushmore; 12. *Family Plot*

....

MULTISCREEN (4)

....

1. *The Long Good Friday*; 2. Jack Dee;
3. Kim Basinger and Alec Baldwin; 4. David Fincher; 5. Basil Brush;
6. Judi Dench's in *Shakespeare in Love*; 7. Sean Connery;
8. *Man About the House*; 9. *Carry on Sergeant*; 10. *Palme d'Or*;
11. The Stig (*Top Gear*); 12. Viggo Mortensen

....

ANSWERS
GEOGRAPHY

....

GLOBETROTTING (1)

....

1. Zurich; 2. Costa Rica; 3. Alluvium; 4. Lake District; 5. Urdu;
6. Kansas; 7. Portugal; 8. Munro; 9. Simón Bolivar; 10. Tibet (China);
11. Neva; 12. Piraeus

....

ROLLING RIVERS

....

1. Severn; 2. South China Sea; 3. Zambezi; 4. Isar; 5. Loire;
6. Warsaw; 7. Dead Sea; 8. Burundi; 9. St Louis; 10. Red River;
11. Gloucestershire; 12. Swan

....

MOUNTAINS HIGH

....

1. Pyrenees; 2. The Rockies; 3. Kilimanjaro; 4. New Zealand;
5. Mt Vinson; 6. Italy; 7. Mt Pico (Pico Island); 8. Mt Elbrus;
9. The Andes; 10. China and Nepal; 11. Scafell Pike; 12. Australia

....

HOW WERE THESE PREVIOUSLY KNOWN? (1)

....

1. Ceylon; 2. Nyasaland; 3. British Honduras; 4. East Pakistan;
5. Siam; 6. Persia; 7. Zaire; 8. New Spain; 9. Gold Coast;
10. Gilbert Islands; 11. Abyssinia; 12. French Sudan

....

ANSWERS
GEOGRAPHY

....

GLOBETROTTING (2)

....

1. Delaware; 2. Italy; 3. Gulf of Mexico; 4. French; 5. Taipei;
6. Lizard Point; 7. Granada; 8. Adelaide; 9. Mt Fujiyama;
10. Zambezi; 11. Maine; 12. Malta, Gozo, Comino

....

WAVING THE FLAG

....

1. Canada's; 2. Red and white; 3. The 13 original colonies;
4. Five; 5. Vertical; 6. Commonwealth Star; 7. Black, red, yellow;
8. Crescent and star; 9. Japan's; 10. Isle of Man's; 11. Green, white,
red; 12. 12

....

ISLANDS OF THE SEA

....

1. Denmark; 2. Scotland; 3. Vancouver Island; 4. South; 5. Dodecanese;
6. Southern Ocean; 7. Nauru; 8. Nine; 9. Borneo; 10. Cook Islands;
11. Chile; 12. Honshu

....

LAKES AND LOCHS

....

1. Italy; 2. Lake Ontario; 3. Bolivia and Peru; 4. Lake Baikal (Russia);
5. Loch Lomond; 6. North Island; 7. France; 8. Sierra Nevada;
9. Michigan, New York, Ohio, Pennsylvania; 10. Caspian Sea;
11. Ullswater; 12. Lake Eyre

....

ANSWERS
GEOGRAPHY

....

LANDMARKS AND MONUMENTS

....

1. Agra; 2. Tunisia; 3. Ponte Vecchio; 4. Georgia; 5. George Washington, Thomas Jefferson, Theodore Roosevelt, Abraham Lincoln; 6. Rotorua; 7. County Antrim; 8. Ayers Rock; 9. Great Dune of Pyla (France); 10. Switzerland; 11. Red Square (Moscow); 12. Peru

....

GLOBETROTTING (3)

....

1. Switzerland and Italy; 2. Amazon; 3. Tallinn; 4. Venezuela; 5. Belgium, France, Germany; 6. Yellowstone; 7. Grand Canal of China; 8. Danube; 9. Herm; 10. France; 11. The Urals; 12. Rome

....

COMING TO TERMS

....

1. Western; 2. Nautical mile; 3. Northern; 4. Confluence; 5. Strength of earthquakes; 6. Mesa; 7. Large waterfall; 8. Archipelago; 9. Lagoon; 10. The study of regional geography; 11. Magma; 12. Valley or ravine

....

SEAS AND OCEANS

....

1. Pacific; 2. Australia and Tasmania; 3. Canada (Bay of Fundy); 4. Dead Sea; 5. Arctic; 6. Strait of Gibraltar; 7. Barents Sea; 8. Coral Sea; 9. Persian Gulf and Gulf of Oman; 10. Pacific; 11. Strait of Magellan; 12. Tyrrhenian Sea

....

ANSWERS
GEOGRAPHY

....

DESERT LANDSCAPES

....

1. Australia; 2. Atlas Mountains; 3. Thar Desert; 4. Antarctica;
5. Mongolia and China; 6. California; 7. 90%;
8. Botswana and Namibia; 9. Atacama Desert (Chile);
10. Western Australia; 11. Mojave (USA); 12. Takla Makan

....

CAPITAL CITIES

....

1. Berlin; 2. Salisbury; 3. Tallahassee; 4. Slovakia;
5. Wellington (NZ); 6. Asunción; 7. Reykjavik (Iceland); 8. Regina;
9. Bismarck; 10. Washington DC; 11. Kigali; 12. La Paz (Bolivia)

....

GLOBETROTTING (4)

....

1. Glen Lyon; 2. Oregon; 3. Quito; 4. Denmark and Sweden; 5. Yalta;
6. Chester; 7. Spice Islands; 8. Belgium; 9. The Orkneys;
10. Fremantle; 11. Elbe; 12. Madrid

....

NAME THEIR CURRENCY

....

1. Rand; 2. Dong; 3. Shekel; 4. Cuban peso; 5. Egyptian pound;
6. Yuan Renmimbi; 7. Rouble; 8. Won; 9. Swiss franc; 10. Real;
11. Danish krone; 12. Tögrög or tugrik

....

ANSWERS
GEOGRAPHY

AIRPORTS OF THE WORLD

1. O'Hare; 2. Amsterdam; 3. Idlewild: 4. Edinburgh Turnhouse;
5. Richard Rogers; 6. Chek Lap Kok; 7. Sydney; 8. Croydon;
9. Marco Polo; 10. Mumbai; 11. Montréal-Trudeau (Pierre Trudeau);
12. Tokyo

HOW WERE THESE PREVIOUSLY KNOWN? (2)

1. Peking; 2. Danzig; 3. Saigon; 4. New Amsterdam; 5. Dacca;
6. Kristiania; 7. Lourenço Marques; 8. Constantinople; 9. Gorky;
10. Edo; 11. Bombay; 12. Leopoldville

BRITISH ISLES

1. Thurso; 2. River Ouse; 3. Leeds; 4. Sandwich, Romney, Dover,
Hythe, Hastings; 5. Fleet; 6. Lindisfarne; 7.Tay; 8. Avebury Circles;
9. The Titan (Derbyshire); 10. Lough Neagh; 11. Mull;
12. Gloucester

GLOBETROTTING (5)

1. Grampians; 2. Corfu; 3. Canada; 4. Trimontaine;
5. Tigris and Euphrates; 6. Seven; 7. Libya; 8. Romania;
9. Bismarck Archipelago; 10. Mt Logan; 11. Murmansk; 12. Mali

ANSWERS
HISTORY

....

WAR AND PEACE

....

1. Eight; 2. Korean War; 3. Battle of Little Big Horn;
4. Britain and Spain; 5. War of American Independence; 6. France;
7. 1746; 8. Iran-Iraqi; 9. 116 years; 10. War of the Spanish Succession;
11. American Civil War; 12. Athens and Sparta

....

WORLD WAR I

....

1. Archduke Franz Ferdinand's; 2. In taxis; 3. Herbert Asquith;
4. Marshal Foch; 5. Tank; 6. Siegfried Sassoon; 7. Gallipoli;
8. Netherlands; 9. Alcohol; 10. General John Pershing;
11. Field Marshal Douglas Haig: 12. Rank and file of the 1914 British
Expeditionary Force

....

WHO SAID THAT?

....

1. Henry Ford; 2. Karl Marx; 3. Oscar Wilde; 4. Adolf Hitler;
5. Duke of Wellington; 6. Richard Nixon; 7. Abraham Lincoln;
8. Napoleon Bonaparte; 9. Harold Macmillan; 10. Elizabeth I;
11. Ronald Reagan; 12. Israeli Defence Minister Moshe Dayan

....

PAST TIMES (1)

....

1. Ireland; 2. First regular bus service; 3. Flatiron Building in
New York; 4. Babylon; 5. The Commonwealth of England (1649-60);
6. Inca; 7. Thomas Cranmer; 8. Horatia; 9. Runnymede, alongside
the Thames; 10. 63 (and seven months); 11. YMCA; 12. 1975

....

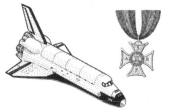

ANSWERS
HISTORY

. . . .

YEARS TO REMEMBER

. . . .

1.1917; 2.1949; 3.1666; 4.1988; 5.1979; 6.1967; 7.1926; 8.1989; 9.1773;
10. 1990; 11.1921; 12.1948

. . . .

KINGS AND QUEENS

. . . .

1. Niece; 2. Alexander III; 3. William the Conqueror (1066);
4. Louis XVI; 5. Jane Seymour; 6. George VI; 7. Richard II;
8. Austrian; 9. James I; 10. King Farouk; 11. Ibn Saud; 12. None

. . . .

BRITISH PRIME MINISTERS

. . . .

1.11; 2. Ramsay MacDonald; 3. Lord Wilson of Rievaulx;
4. Benjamin Disraeli; 5. Spencer Perceval; 6. Stanley Baldwin;
7. 24; 8. Four; 9. Andrew Bonar Law; 10. James;
11. David Lloyd George; 12. Sir Alec Douglas-Home

. . . .

THE 1960s

. . . .

1. 1961; 2. John Glenn; 3. *The Sun*; 4. Gary Powers; 5. Rachel Carson's;
6. Malcolm X; 7. 1966; 8. Felt-tip pen; 9. Prague Spring;
10. Golda Meir; 11. Pelican crossings; 12. Bolivia

. . . .

HOW WERE THESE BETTER KNOWN?

. . . .

1. Lenin; 2. The Red Baron; 3. Malcolm X; 4. La Pasionaria;
5. Buddha; 6. Lawrence of Arabia; 7. Mother Teresa; 8. El Cid;
9. Lord Haw Haw; 10. Leon Trotsky; 11. Pol Pot; 12. Tito

. . . .

ANSWERS
HISTORY

PAST TIMES (2)

1. 1904; 2. Thomas Paine; 3. British Commonwealth; 4. Black Bess;
5. 1984; 6. 1847; 7. Amelia Earhart; 8. Mary Baker Eddy; 9. Hungary;
10. Boer leader Paul Kruger; 11. Pat Garrett; 12. Dutch

MORE KINGS AND QUEENS

1. Albania; 2. Queen Salote; 3. Edward III; 4. Anne of Cleves; 5. 18;
6. Iceni; 7. Edward VII; 8. Umberto II; 9. James I of England;
10. 21 April 1926; 11. Mary Queen of Scots; 12. Alexander II

PAST TIMES (3)

1. An Englishman named Edward Teach; 2. Trygve Lie; 3. Republican;
4. Alaska; 5. Adrian IV; 6. Robert E Lee's; 7. The Althing in Iceland;
8. 17th; 9. Cleveland, Ohio; 10. Anastasia; 11. Malta; 12. St Alban

THE 1970s

1. Salvador Allende; 2. Cigarette advertising; 3. Richard Nixon;
4. A knighthood; 5. Mother Teresa; 6. Spiro Agnew; 7. 1974;
8. Angela Rippon; 9. Patricia Hearst; 10. Idi Amin; 11. Anthony Blunt;
12. Edward Heath

MORE YEARS TO REMEMBER

1. 1963; 2. 1969; 3. 1941; 4. 1916; 5. 1971; 6. 1982; 7. 1947; 8. 1849;
9. 1837; 10. 1649; 11. 1900; 12. 1854

MILITARY MEN

1. Napoleon and Wellington; 2. The Carthaginian; 3. Wing Commander Guy Gibson; 4. John Churchill, Duke of Marlborough; 5. General Norman Schwarzkopf; 6. General Dwight D Eisenhower; 7. The Black Prince; 8. Ulysses Simpson Grant; 9. Norfolk; 10. Marshal Zhukov; 11. 23; 12. General James Wolfe

AMERICAN PRESIDENTS

1. Milhous; 2. Jimmy Carter; 3. James Garfield; 4. John Adams; 5. Thomas Jefferson; 6. James Buchanan; 7. Abraham Lincoln; 8. William Henry Harrison; 9. Andrew Jackson; 10. Harry S Truman; 11. John Adams and Thomas Jefferson; 12. Senator John Kerry

FAMOUS EXPLORERS

1. *Golden Hind*; 2. 1492; 3. Westminster Abbey; 4. Vivian Fuchs; 5. Australia; 6. Vasco da Gama; 7. Wales; 8. Marco Polo; 9. Reaching the summit of Mt Everest; 10. Richard Burton; 11. The Niger; 12. Amerigo Vespucci

NICKNAMES

1. Duke of Wellington; 2. Harold Macmillan; 3. Attila the Hun; 4. President François Duvalier of Haiti; 5. Napoleon Bonaparte; 6. General Erwin Rommel; 7. Georges Clemenceau; 8. General George S Patton; 9. Judge Jeffreys; 10. Otto von Bismarck; 11. Louis XIV of France; 12. King Edward I of England

ANSWERS

HISTORY

THE 1980s

1. Columbia; 2. Iranian; 3. Mark Chapman; 4. Its bicentenary;
5. The tanker *Exxon Valdez*; 6. 1986; 7. Kurt Waldheim;
8. Michael Dukakis; 9. Grenada; 10. François Mitterrand;
11. US advertising; 12. 1987

WORLD WAR II

1. The planned invasion of Britain; 2. Barnes Wallis;
3. Reich Marshal; 4. General William Slim; 5. 1942; 6. Rudolf Hess;
7. French Resistance; 8. Herbert Morrison and John Anderson;
9. General Douglas MacArthur; 10. Captain Charles Upham (NZ);
11. Marshal Pétain; 12. 56

ANCIENT WORLD

1. Helen of Troy's; 2. Caligula; 3. Cyrus the Great; 4. Athens;
5. Emperor Hadrian's; 6. Vulcan; 7. Macedonia; 8. Spartacus;
9. By drinking hemlock; 10. Julius Caesar; 11. Persians and Greeks;
12. Cicero

PAST TIMES (4)

1. Hyde Park; 2. Benito Mussolini's; 3. Tutankhamun's tomb;
4. She threw herself under the king's horse at the Derby;
5. Martin Luther; 6. Richard Cromwell; 7. 14th;
8. The evacuation of Dunkirk; 9. Melbourne, Australia;
10. Kemal Atatürk; 11. Ming; 12. Pigeon post

ANSWERS
MUSIC

POP DUOS

1. Nicole Kidman; 2. Jordan and Peter Andre; 3. Serge Gainsbourg and Jane Birkin; 4. Romania; 5. Pamela Anderson; 6. Peters and Lee; 7. Mariah Carey and Whitney Houston; 8. Lennon and McCartney; 9. Kermit the Frog; 10. Esther and Abi Ofarim; 11. Danish; 12. Alison Mosshart and Jamie Hince

WHO DID THEY BECOME?

1. Shakin' Stevens; 2. Barry Manilow; 3. Chris de Burgh; 4. Blur; 5. Snoop Doggy Dogg; 6. Cliff Richard; 7. Tina Turner; 8. Meat Loaf; 9. Marty Wilde; 10. Cat Stevens (then Yusef Islam); 11. Procol Harum; 12. Adam Faith

THE BEATLES

1. The Quarrymen; 2. Decca; 3. Julian Lennon; 4. Paul McCartney and Ringo Starr; 5. Paul McCartney; 6. "Michelle"; 7. Jesus; 8. Peter Sellers; 9. Beatles' manager Brian Epstein; 10. Paul McCartney; 11. The Ed Sullivan Show; 12. "The Ballad Of John And Yoko"

POP GOES CHRISTMAS

1. Slade; 2. "When A Child Is Born"; 3. Travis; 4. "Christmas Alphabet"; 5. Barry Manilow; 6. Frank Sinatra; 7. 1984; 8. "All I Want For Christmas Is My Two Front Teeth"; 9. George Harrison; 10. *Meet Me In St Louis*; 11. "Christmas Auld Lang Syne"; 12. "Santa's List"

ANSWERS
MUSIC

....

POP GOES THE 60s

....

1. Gene Pitney; 2. Jonathan King; 3. Phil and Don; 4. Glen Campbell;
5. "(I Can't Get No) Satisfaction"; 6. 1967; 7. 14; 8. Stevie Wonder;
9. Lulu; 10. Carl Wilson; 11. Shangri-Las; 12. Frank and Nancy Sinatra

....

MUSICAL MEDLEY (1)

....

1. Annie Lennox; 2. James; 3. Che Guevara; 4. Five; 5. The Bolshoi;
6. Frankie Laine; 7. Leicester; 8. Sandie Shaw; 9. Marian Anderson;
10. Rod Stewart; 11. Donny Osmond; 12. Aretha Franklin

....

ONE HIT WONDERS

....

1. Shorty Long; 2. The Flowerpot Men; 3. Napoleon XIV; 4. "Doop";
5. Hale and Pace; 6. Clive Dunn; 7. "Nut Rocker"; 8. Lee Marvin;
9. The Archies; 10. Sir Douglas Quintet; 11. By saying "Eh-Oh!";
12. Artist L S Lowry

....

COLOUR THESE SONGS

....

1. Yellow; 2. Black; 3. Orange; 4. Indigo; 5. Ebony; 6. Pink; 7. Blue;
8. Purple; 9. Green; 10. Pink; 11. Blue; 12. Gold

....

POP GOES THE 70S

....

1. Nancy Spungen; 2. 10cc; 3. "Breaking Up Is Hard To Do"; 4. "Hot
Love"; 5. 27; 6. "Got To Be There"; 7. "Down Down"; 8. Linda Ronstadt;
9. "Love To Love You"; 10. 1977; 11. Nine; 12. Warren Beatty

....

ANSWERS
MUSIC

MUSICAL MEDLEY (2)

1. The Crickets; 2. John Michael Osbourne; 3. "Abbey Road";
4. Amsterdam; 5. Phyllis Nelson; 6. Mike Oldfield; 7. Trombone;
8. Florenz Ziegfeld's; 9. *Dick Tracy*; 10. Sir Hubert Parry;
11. Winston; 12. W S Gilbert

ALL THAT JAZZ

1. Humphrey Lyttelton; 2. Trumpet; 3. Charlie Parker; 4. Glenn Miller;
5. Bessie Smith; 6. Satchmo (Louis Armstrong); 7. Benny Goodman;
8. Billie Holiday; 9. Duke Ellington, Earl Hines, Count Basie;
10. Dave Brubeck; 11. Ronnie Scott; 12. *Jazz on a Summer's Day*

UNDER THE BATON

1. André Previn; 2. Sir Henry Wood; 3. Leopold Stokowski;
4. Philadelphia; 5. Sir John Barbirolli; 6. Sir Thomas Beecham;
7. Liverpool; 8. Herbert von Karajan; 9. Sir Edward Heath;
10. Leonard Bernstein; 11. Sir Roger Norrington; 12. Sue Perkins

POP GOES THE 80S

1. Musical Youth; 2. "The Chicken Song"; 3. 1986; 4. Paul Weller;
5. 25; 6. *Moonstruck*; 7. "I Want Your Sex"; 8. Madonna;
9. Christie Brinkley; 10. "Making Up Your Mind";
11. "I Should Be So Lucky"; 12. "Desire"

ANSWERS
MUSIC

··

101 MUSICAL MEDLEY (3)

··

1. Bryan Ferry; 2. Saxophone; 3. Sergei Prokofiev; 4. Tim Rice;
5. Empty orchestra; 6. The Police; 7. *Holiday Inn;* 8. Ivor Novello;
9. The Priests; 10. June Carter; 11. Arthur Sullivan;
12. Katherine Jenkins and Darcey Bussell

102 MUSIC FROM THE MOVIES

··

1. John Williams; 2. Zither; 3. *The Thomas Crown Affair* (original);
4. Dario Marianelli; 5. Clint Eastwood; 6. Gladys Knight;
7. "The Colonel Bogey March"; 8. Scott Joplin's; 9. Vangelis;
10. *An Inconvenient Truth*; 11. Henry Mancini; 12. Maurice Jarre

103 GRAND OPERA

··

1. Gioacchino Rossini; 2. Milan La Scala; 3. Four;
4. Major female singer; 5. Jacques Offenbach; 6. William Schwenck;
7. Madame Butterfly; 8. *Billy Budd*; 9. Opera singer; 10. Libretto;
11. Joan Sutherland; 12. *Otello* and *Falstaff*

104 WHO COMPOSED THESE CLASSICS?

··

1. Sergei Prokofiev; 2. Camille Saint-Saëns; 3. Benjamin Britten;
4. George Frederic Handel; 5. Maurice Ravel; 6. Aaron Copland;
7. Claude Debussy; 8. Edward Elgar; 9. John Philip Sousa;
10. Johannes Brahms; 11. Jean Sibelius; 12. Frederick Delius

ANSWERS
MUSIC

· ·

POP GOES THE 90s
· ·

1. Hanson; 2. Prince; 3. Robson and Jerome; 4. Sheryl Crow; 5. "Diva";
6. "Emergency On Planet Earth"; 7. Wigan; 8. Phil Collins; 9. Sting;
10. Radiohead; 11. *Four Weddings and a Funeral*; 12. Rita Coolidge

· ·

MUSICAL MEDLEY (4)
· ·

1. Léo Delibes; 2. Ravi Shankar; 3. Moon River; 4. "Kontiki"; 5. Belgian;
6. Bernie Taupin; 7. Mary Martin; 8. The Beastie Boys;
9. Micky Dolenz; 10. *Kid Galahad;* 11. Jamie Cullum's; 12. New Zealand

· ·

CLASSICAL NUMBERS
· ·

1. The Emperor; 2. Joseph Haydn; 3. Antonio Vivaldi; 4. Nine; 5. 20;
6. No 2; 7. 88; 8. Seven; 9. 35; 10. No 5; 11. Five; 12. Napoleon's retreat
from Moscow

· ·

ROCK ON
· ·

1. Chris Blackwell; 2. Fairport Convention; 3. Jethro Tull;
4. Jimmy Cliff; 5. 1995; 6. B-52s; 7. George Michael's; 8. Bob Marley;
9. The Buggles; 10. David Bowie; 11. "Relax"; 12. Woodstock

· ·

MUSICAL MEDLEY (5)
· ·

1. "All I Really Want To Do"; 2. Paris; 3. Harlem; 4. Elmer Bernstein;
5. Bob Geldof; 6. "Happy Birthday To You"; 7. Mark Knopfler; 8. Violin;
9. Peter Gabriel; 10. Drum; 11. Matt Monro; 12. Richard Clayderman

· ·

ANSWERS
PEOPLE

ALL SORTS (1)

1. Dennis Potter; 2. Thomas Edison; 3. Salvatori Lombino;
4. Dr Andrei Sakharov; 5. George Bernard Shaw; 6. James Madison;
7. Parker and Barrow; 8. Bear Grylls; 9. Roland Garros;
10. Roald Amundsen; 11. Mary Wilson; 12. Adrian Anthony

WHICH GEORGE?

1. George Michael; 2. George Bernard Shaw; 3. George Washington;
4. George Cole; 5. George Sand; 6. George Harrison; 7. George Best;
8. George Gershwin; 9. George Lucas; 10. George Marshall;
11. George Stevens; 12. George Clooney

THE ROYAL FAMILY

1. Mustique; 2. Princess Michael of Kent; 3. Princess Eugenie;
4. Prince Philip (in 1961); 5. Princess Anne's; 6. James Callaghan;
7. Duke of Gloucester; 8. 21 June; 9. 1976; 10. Duke and Duchess of
York; 11. Henry Charles Albert David Wales; 12. Ruthie Henshall

FAMOUS FIRSTS

1. Charles Lindbergh; 2. Nancy Astor; 3. Roger Bannister;
4. Queen Victoria; 5. Valentina Tereshkova; 6. David Ben-Gurion;
7. Alexander Graham Bell; 8. Len Hutton; 9. Henry VII;
10. Nancy Pelosi; 11. Joshua Slocum; 12. Captain Matthew Webb

ANSWERS
PEOPLE

WIVES OF PRESIDENTS

1. Raisa; 2. Martha Washington; 3. Carla Bruni; 4. Jimmy Carter's;
5. Imelda Marcos; 6. Winnie Mandela; 7. Lady Bird Johnson;
8. Eva Perón; 9. Jackie Kennedy; 10. Betty Ford; 11. Elena Ceauşescu;
12. Eleanor Roosevelt

ALL SORTS (2)

1. Lenny Bruce; 2. Zechariah; 3. Amy Johnson; 4. Julia Ward Howe;
5. Walker; 6. Clarence Birdseye; 7. Douglas (Noel) Adams; 8. Howard
Hughes; 9. General Mark Clark; 10. Standard Oil; 11. Kim Philby;
12. René Descartes

WHOSE LAST WORDS WERE THESE?

1. Elizabeth I; 2. Humphrey Bogart; 3. Anna Pavlova;
4. Charles Foster Kane in *Citizen Kane*; 5. Heinrich Heine;
6. Prince Albert; 7. Emperor Caligula; 8. Phineas T Barnum;
9. Lord Palmerston; 10. Ludwig van Beethoven; 11. Bing Crosby;
12. Hamlet

HEROES AND HEROINES

1. Admiral Nelson's (Trafalgar Day); 2. Edith Cavell; 3. Audie Murphy;
4. Major Pat Reid; 5. Group Captain Leonard Cheshire; 6. Lt Col
Herbert Jones; 7. Florence Nightingale; 8. Odette Sansom; 9. Malta;
10. Paul Revere; 11. Robert the Bruce; 12. Captain Lawrence Oates (on
walking out into the blizzard on Captain Scott's ill-fated expedition)

ANSWERS
PEOPLE

....

WHICH JOHN?

....

1. Johnny Cash; 2. John Wilkes Booth; 3. Johnny Depp;
4. John Updike; 5. Johnny Carson; 6. King John; 7. John Smith;
8. John Williams; 9. John Terry; 10. John Mills;
11. John Maynard Keynes; 12. John Dillinger

....

ALL SORTS (3)

....

1. Elizabeth Barrett and Robert Browning; 2. Blenheim Palace;
3. Ivan the Terrible (Ivan IV); 4. Klapka; 5. David Walliams;
6. René Goscinny; 7. Branwell Brontë; 8. BBC Sports Personality of
the Year; 9. Margaret Drabble; 10. Alexander Pope; 11. Morrissey;
12 Robert Webb

....

WHO DID THESE BECOME?

....

1. Pope Benedict XVI; 2. Bill Clinton; 3. Ho Chi Minh; 4. Elvis Costello;
5. Buffalo Bill; 6. Omar Sharif; 7. Joseph Stalin; 8. Julie Andrews;
9. Confucius; 10. Calamity Jane; 11. Bill Wyman; 12. Meg Ryan

....

CRIME ON THEIR MIND

....

1. Jack Ruby; 2. Ronnie Biggs; 3. Timothy McVeigh; 4. George Blake;
5. James Earl Ray; 6. Ship-to-shore telegraph; 7. John Haigh;
8. Income-tax evasion; 9. John Christie;
10. Henri Charrière's (Papillon); 11. Art forgery; 12. Ronald Reagan

....

··

HOME SWEET HOME

··

1. Devonshire; 2. San Simeon; 3. British foreign secretary's;
4. Rudyard Kipling; 5. Elysée Palace; 6. Mary Pickford and Douglas
Fairbanks'; 7. George Washington's; 8. Osborne House;
9. Duke of Wellington's; 10. Daphne Du Maurier's; 11. Chartwell;
12. Sir Robert Walpole

··

ALL SORTS (4)

··

1. W C Field's; 2. Alfred, Lord Tennyson; 3. Bobby Fischer; 4. Chicago;
5. Ambrose Bierce; 6. Vidkun Quisling (leader of the Norwegian
Fascist Party); 7. Dr Richard Beeching's; 8. Kenneth Branagh and
Emma Thompson; 9. Czechoslovakia; 10. Florence Griffith-Joyner;
11. Cambodia; 12. Lord Tweedsmuir

··

SHOWBIZ SIBLINGS: ADD THE SURNAME

··

1. Baldwin; 2. Affleck; 3. Beverley; 4. Everly; 5. Gyllenhaal; 6. Ross;
7. Roberts; 8. Kemp; 9. Arquette; 10. Estevez; 11. Sawalha; 12. Wilson

··

WHOSE NICKNAMES?

··

1. Robert Maxwell; 2. Queen Mary I; 3. Muhammad Ali;
4. Frank Sinatra; 5. Michael Heseltine; 6. Dudley Moore;
7. Eric Bristow; 8. William H Bonney; 9. Sarah Bernhardt;
10. Tony Blair; 11. Sylvester Stallone; 12. Imelda Marcos

··

ANSWERS
PEOPLE

....

WHAT A SCANDAL!

....

1. Robin Cook; 2. Linda Tripp; 3. Boris Becker; 4. John Stonehouse;
5. Jimmy Swaggart; 6. Naomi Campbell; 7. Martha Stewart;
8. Lana Turner's; 9. California's list of top tax evaders;
10. The Clermont Club; 11. Norman Scott; 12. Perjury

....

ALL SORTS (5)

....

1. Orville and Wilbur; 2. 2000; 3. St Jude; 4. Oliver Reed;
5. William Burroughs; 6. William Rushton; 7. The Artful Dodger;
8. Marilyn Monroe; 9. Franz Joseph Haydn; 10. Lech Wałęsa;
11. Anne Robinson; 12. George Bush

....

WHO SAID THESE?

....

1. George W Bush; 2. Groucho Marx; 3. Harold Macmillan;
4. Gerald Ford; 5. John Lennon; 6. Woody Allen; 7. Charles De Gaulle;
8. Richard Nixon; 9. Adolf Hitler; 10. Billy Connolly;
11. Henry Kissinger; 12. Margaret Thatcher

....

WHICH SMITH?

....

1. Harvey Smith; 2. Dodie Smith; 3. Ian Smith; 4. Sydney Smith;
5. Stan Smith; 6. John Smith; 7. Steve Smith; 8. Stevie Smith;
9. Liz Smith; 10. Paul Smith; 11. Adam Smith; 12. Cyril Smith

....

ANSWERS

PEOPLE

THE IMMORTALS

1. Narcissus; 2. Apollo; 3. 12; 4. Prometheus; 5. Poseidon; 6. Thor;
7. Golden apple; 8. Odysseus (or Ulysses); 9. Charon; 10. Bastet;
11. Midas; 12. Hermes

ALL SORTS (6)

1. John Brown's; 2. H M Stanley; 3. Arthur Conan Doyle;
4. Thomas De Quincey; 5. Valentine Dyall; 6. Ireland;
7. Lord Baden-Powell; 8. Anthony Shaffer;
9. Baroness Thatcher of Kesteven; 10. Keith; 11. Joan Collins;
12. Dorothy Parker

ANSWERS
SCIENCE & NATURE

· ·

RANDOM SAMPLE (1)

· ·

1. Brassica; 2. Lodge; 3. Smell; 4. Trepanning; 5. Radioactivity;
6. Watercress; 7. Cow (*vacca*); 8. Ozone; 9. Dog (called Laika);
10. Study of glands; 11. Pig; 12. Penguin

PLANTS AND TREES

· ·

1. Deadly Nightshade; 2. Cucumber; 3. Snakewood; 4. Yew;
5. Stamen; 6. Three; 7. Algae; 8. Poppy; 9. Coconut;
10. Venus Fly Trap; 11. Yeast; 12. Underground

AMONG THE ANIMALS

· ·

1. Grasshopper; 2. Hair; 3. Bottom of sea or lake; 4. Polar;
5. Webbed; 6. Fox; 7. Sett; 8. Koala; 9. Hummingbird;
10. Male donkey and female horse; 11. Spiders; 12. Beetle

IDENTIFY THE MISSING COLLECTIVE NAMES

· ·

1. Dolphins; 2. Toads; 3. Piglets; 4. Budgerigars; 5. Tigers;
6. Giraffes; 7. Locusts; 8. Jellyfish; 9. Cats; 10. Pheasants;
11. Rhinoceros; 12. Magpies

THE HUMAN BODY

· ·

1. Femur (thighbone); 2. Neck; 3. Four; 4. Ear; 5. Kidneys; 6. 46;
7. Rapid Eye Movement; 8. Both have 24; 9. Right; 10. Skin;
11. Gristle; 12. Pancreas

· ·

RANDOM SAMPLE (2)

· ·

1. Joseph Black; 2. Finch; 3. Mulberry leaves;
4. Gene Cernan (Apollo 17, 1972); 5. Bee hummingbird; 6. Pink;
7. Irish Moss; 8. Large Hadron Collider (LHC); 9. Rodent; 10. Dry ice;
11. Copper and tin; 12. Kookaburra

WEATHER WISE

· ·

1. Rainfall; 2. Cirrus; 3. Eight; 4. Winds; 5. Air pressure;
6. Anti-cyclone; 7. Intensity of an earthquake; 8. South of Ireland;
9. Katrina; 10. Counter-clockwise; 11. 1952;
12. Another 40 days of rain

MORE PLANTS AND TREES

· ·

1. Grass; 2. Japan; 3. Sphagnum; 4. New Zealand; 5. Sepal;
6. Sweet Chestnut; 7. Chinese Gooseberry; 8. Daffodil; 9. Fungus;
10. Its bark; 11. Stigma; 12. Africa

FURTHER AMONG THE ANIMALS

· ·

1. Adder (or Viper); 2. Calf; 3. Honeybee; 4. Rodent; 5. Mauritius;
6. Velvet; 7. Red; 8. Wolf; 9. Dog; 10. Pipistrelle; 11. Otter's;
12. Manatee

ANSWERS
SCIENCE & NATURE

. . . .

RANDOM SAMPLE (3)
. . . .

1. Young salmon or trout; 2. Tuberculosis; 3. Rabbits; 4. Ice;
5. Vitamin D; 6. X-ray; 7. Laughing gas; 8. Nuclear energy;
9. Hypertext Mark-up Language; 10. 22; 11. Chrysalis; 12. Hydrogen

. . . .

MAXI AND MINI
. . . .

1. Cheetah; 2. Condor; 3. Diplodocus; 4. Blue whale; 5. African;
6. Mayfly; 7. Jackfruit; 8. Sloth; 9. Reticulated python; 10. Komodo
dragon; 11. Chan's Megastick (stick insect); 12. Peregrine falcon

. . . .

MEDICAL MATTERS
. . . .

1. Hippocrates; 2. Glandular fever; 3. Mumps; 4. Chicken-pox;
5. Quinine; 6. Christiaan Barnard; 7. 1978; 8. CAT scan;
9. Heart attack; 10. Plaster of Paris; 11. Colour blindness; 12. Foxglove

. . . .

THE UNIVERSE
. . . .

1. The Hubble; 2. Jupiter; 3. Exploding star; 4. Boiling; 5. Hale-Bopp;
6. The Sun; 7. Andromeda; 8. Hydrogen; 9. Eight minutes (approx);
10. Venus; 11. The Moon; 12. *Aurora borealis*

. . . .

RANDOM SAMPLE (4)
. . . .

1. Chlorophyll; 2. Rabies; 3. On its toes; 4. V; 5. Moth; 6. Minus 18°;
7. Nitrogen; 8. San Francisco; 9. Frequency Modulated;
10. J Robert Oppenheimer; 11. Vitamin C; 12. Dolly

. . . .

ANSWERS
SCIENCE & NATURE

· ·

MORE OF THE HUMAN BODY

· ·

1. Ear (stapedius); 2. Voice box; 3. Cornea; 4. 100,000;
5. Fontanelles; 6. Outermost layer of the skin; 7.Tip; 8. Incisors,
Canines, Molars; 9. Muscle (back); 10. Hearing; 11. Ulna nerve;
12. Tooth enamel

GIANTS OF SCIENCE

· ·

1. Marie and Pierre Curie; 2. Isaac Newton; 3. Joseph Priestley;
4. Penicillin; 5. Sigmund Freud; 6. Edward Jenner; 7. Galileo Galilei;
8. Ernest Rutherford; 9. William Harvey; 10. Joseph Lister;
11. His theory of relativity; 12. Polish

PHOBIAS : WHAT ARE YOU AFRAID OF?

· ·

1. Cats; 2. Foreigners; 3. Speed; 4. Spiders; 5. Computers;
6. Marriage; 7. Bees; 8. Horses; 9. Water; 10. Strong light;
11. Being stared at; 12. Fear of becoming phobic

RANDOM SAMPLE (5)

· ·

1. Drey; 2. Mercury; 3. Digital Versatile Disc; 4. Head;
5. Royal Observatory, Greenwich; 6. Holt; 7. Carbon; 8. Bear;
9. Samuel Morse; 10. Common Lobster; 11. Egypt; 12. Magpie

ANSWERS
SCIENCE & NATURE

....

STRANGE BUT TRUE

....

1. To mate with virgin queens; 2. Human flea; 3. Barnacle;
4. Newfoundland; 5. Mudskipper; 6. St Kilda; 7. Seabirds; 8. Eight;
9. Seahorse; 10. Blowfly (bluebottle); 11. Electric eel; 12. Their wings

....

GREAT INVENTORS

....

1. John Logie Baird; 2. World Wide Web; 3. George Stephenson;
4. Turbo-jet engine; 5. Samuel Colt; 6. Hovercraft; 7. Guglielmo
Marconi; 8. The pencil; 9. Johannes Gutenberg's (printing press);
10. James Dyson; 11. Daniel Fahrenheit; 12. Polaroid

....

WHAT WOULD YOU BE STUDYING?

....

1. Volcanoes; 2. Insects; 3. Feet; 4. Earthquakes; 5. Shells;
6. Whales and dolphins; 7. Ears; 8. Early humans; 9. Clouds;
10. Weights and measures; 11. The sun; 12. Rain

....

RANDOM SAMPLE (6)

....

1. Marsupial; 2. Electrical resistance; 3. Structure of DNA;
4. Ospreys; 5. Sirius; 6. Froghopper; 7. Leveret; 8. Sn; 9. Stethoscope;
10. Dandelion; 11. Potato; 12. Iceberg

....

ANSWERS
SPORTS & GAMES

SPORTING CHANCE (1)

1. Tourist Trophy; 2. Boxer Bob Fitzsimmons (1902); 3. 26; 4. Chess;
5. Astronaut Alan Shepard (1971); 6. Graham and Damon Hill;
7. Peterborough United; 8. Water skiing; 9. Crossbow (bolt); 10. 1964;
11. Eight; 12. Scars

CRICKET: 1ST INNINGS

1. 1864; 2. 10ft (3.05m); 3. Nelson; 4. Alan Knott; 5. Colin Cowdrey;
6. Chappell-Hadlee Trophy; 7. Viv Richards; 8. 136; 9. Ten; 10. 1989;
11. Brentwood; 12. By cutting the turf

FOOTBALL: 1ST HALF

1. Sir Stanley Matthews (1964); 2. Australia's football team;
3. 1954; 4. Plymouth Argyle; 5. Pelé; 6. Marco Materazzi;
7. Chester City (it is partly in Wales, partly in England);
8. Sheikh Mansour bin Zayed Al Nahyan; 9. Martin Keown;
10. An orange ball; 11. Queen of the South;
12. They were beaten 1-0 by USA

GOLF: 1ST ROUND

1. Woods, irons, putters; 2. Two strokes under par on a hole;
3. Curtis Cup; 4. 4.25in; 5. Bob Charles; 6. Greg Norman;
7. Trevor Immelman; 8. 1927; 9. Karrie Webb; 10. Hole in one;
11. The Bronx in New York; 12. Byron Nelson

ANSWERS
SPORTS & GAMES

....

RUGBY: 1ST HALF

....

1.Toulouse; 2. Tri-Series; 3. Northampton; 4. Wing forward;
5. John Smit (SA); 6. Scotland; 7. Ospreys; 8. Oxford and Cambridge;
9. John Dawes; 10. Northern Bulls; 11. Melted-down rupees;
12. Jean-Pierre Rives

....

SPORTING CHANCE (2)

....

1. 147; 2. Pete Sampras; 3. Tom Lehman; 4. Wilheim Steinitz;
5. Begin; 6. Cowboys; 7. Canada; 8. Seven; 9. Rocky Graziano;
10. Rugby league; 11. Cycling; 12. Zara Phillips

....

MOTOR RACING: 1ST LAP

....

1. 2006 (Hungarian); 2. San Marino; 3. Giuseppe Farina (1950);
4. That a faster car is trying to overtake; 5. Brazilian;
6. Driver error; 7. Le Mans; 8. Monza; 9. Jochen Rindt (who died
earlier in the season but never lost his lead); 10. Alain Prost;
11. Plane crash; 12. Lotus

....

TENNIS: 1ST SET

....

1. Jamie; 2. 3ft (0.914m); 3. 167; 4. Monica Seles; 5. Roche;
6. Wimbledon; 7. Because of the frilly underwear she wore on court;
8. Boris Becker (1985); 9. John Lloyd; 10. Spain; 11. Billie Jean Moffitt;
12. Laura Robson

....

ANSWERS
SPORTS & GAMES

THE OLYMPICS

1. The five continents; 2. 1908; 3. Ben Johnson; 4. 26 miles/42km;
5. Johnny Weissmuller (Tarzan in the movies) won five for
swimming; 6. Because of the USSR's invasion of Hungary;
7. Los Angeles (1984); 8. Peter Snell (NZ); 9. Nadia Comaneci;
10. 1960 (Rome); 11. Dutch athlete Fanny Blankers-Koen; 12. 19

SPORTING CHANCE (3)

1. O J Simpson; 2. James Graham; 3. 18 inches; 4. Basketball; 5. Two;
6. Cresta Run; 7. Seven weeks; 8. Clay; 9. The Honourable Company of
Edinburgh Golfers; 10. Rook; 11. 1999; 12. Evander Holyfield's

WHOSE NICKNAMES ARE THESE?

1. Marcus Trescothick; 2. James J Corbett; 3. Ernie Els;
4. Maureen Connolly; 5. Gordon Durie; 6. Andrew Strauss;
7. Will Carling; 8. Fred Couples; 9. Joe Frazier; 10. Martin Offiah;
11. Lance Klusener; 12. Ronnie O'Sullivan

CRICKET: 2ND INNINGS

1. USA v Canada (1844); 2. Sir Richard Hadlee; 3. Australia; 4. Eight;
5. Bowls; 6. Market garden; 7. Glenn McGrath; 8. Derek Underwood;
9. Everton Weekes; 10. Martlet, six; 11. Mike Gatting, John Emburey,
Chris Cowdrey, Graham Gooch; 12. John Keats

ANSWERS
SPORTS & GAMES

. . . .

FOOTBALL: 2ND HALF

. . . .

1. Gordon Strachan; 2. 125; 3. Diego Maradona talking about
Carlos Tevez; 4. Didier Drogba; 5. West Ham FC; 6. Engineering and
economics; 7. Manchester City goalkeeper Bert Trautmann, who
played on in the 1956 FA Cup final with a broken neck;
8. Ronald Reagan; 9. Rio Ferdinand; 10. Franz Beckenbauer;
11. Tottenham Hotspur (1983); 12. Dave Beasant (for Wimbledon v
Liverpool, 1988)

SPORTING CHANCE (4)

. . . .

1. The Bourda Oval, Georgetown; 2. Bully-off; 3. Steve Cauthen;
4. Five; 5. Rams; 6. Three; 7. Melbourne; 8. Justin Langer; 9. Four;
10. Fencing; 11. Northampton Town; 12. Colin Meads

GOLF: 2ND ROUND

. . . .

1. St Andrews; 2. Green jacket; 3. 14; 4. Percy Alliss; 5. 1979;
6. Albatross; 7. Arnold Palmer; 8. Philadelphia Cricket Club;
9. Nick Faldo; 10. Sir Henry Cotton's; 11. Padriag Harrington;
12. Greenland

RUGBY: 2ND HALF

. . . .

1. Rugby Sevens World Cup; 2. Neath (1971); 3. Delon and Steffon;
4. France (1900); 5. Great Britain; 6. Streaker Erica Roe;
7. *Talonneur;* 8. Ten; 9. Jonathan Davies; 10. Fabien Pelous;
11. It ended up a five-way tie; 12. St Helens

ANSWERS
SPORTS & GAMES

··

170 PLAYING GAMES

··

1. 18; 2. Amongst British Army officers in India;
3. Cardinal (the rest are chess pieces); 4. Cribbage; 5. 64; 6. Bridge;
7. Mah Jong; 8. Royal Flush; 9. Pit; 10. 13 tricks by one team;
11. Pink; 12. Backgammon

··

171 SPORTING CHANCE (5)

··

1. England and Scotland; 2. High jump; 3. Three; 4. 1903;
5. Swimming stroke; 6. Uruguay; 7. Harold Abrahams and Eric
Liddell; 8. Logs; 9. Wrestling hold; 10. 1829; 11. Mark Spitz;
12. Harrow School

··

172 SPORTING VENUES

··

1. Wigan Warriors; 2. Longchamp; 3. Maracanã; 4. Napier (NZ);
5. White City; 6. Bank Street; 7. Kinshasa (Zaire); 8. Wrigley Field;
9. Golf; 10. Woolloongabba (Brisbane); 11. Milan;
12. Brooklands (Surrey)

··

173 MOTOR RACING: 2ND LAP

··

1. John Surtees; 2. South African; 3. Archie Scott Brown;
4. Jim Clark's; 5. Six-wheeled car; 6. Mike Hawthorn (1958);
7. Tom Kristensen; 8. Donington Park; 9. James Hunt;
10. Indianapolis 500; 11. Benetton; 12. Max Mosley

··

ANSWERS
SPORTS & GAMES

....

TENNIS: 2ND SET

....

1. Venus; 2. Althea Gibson (1957); 3. Steffi Graf; 4. Flushing Meadows;
5. George VI (when Duke of York); 6. Rod Laver (1962, 1969);
7. Pete Sampras; 8. Evonne Goolagong; 9. Mark Philippoussis;
10. Tracy Austin; 11. Bill Tilden; 12. Cypriot

....

BROTHERS IN SPORT: ADD THE SURNAMES

....

1. Underwood; 2. Pathan; 3. Fashanu; 4. Pollock; 5. Hastings;
6. Schumacher; 7. Neville; 8. Hollioake; 9. Lloyd; 10. Lobbe;
11. Cooper; 12. De Boer

....

SPORTING CHANCE (6)

....

1. The America's Cup (1851); 2. Winning the world championships in
Formula One and CART; 3. Zola Budd; 4. Jaroslav Drobny;
5. Show-jumping obstacle; 6. New Zealand; 7. Spain; 8. 1980;
9. *This Sporting Life;* 10. Polo; 11. Once; 12. Tonga (2007)

....

ANSWERS
GENERAL KNOWLEDGE

....

NUMBER 1

....

1. Electrocardiogram; 2. Salmon; 3. New Zealand; 4. 73; 5. 28;
6. Isle of Man; 7. Mothballs; 8. Tooth decay; 9. Cointreau;
10. Vibraphone; 11. Wat Tyler; 12. Albemarle Street

....

NUMBER 2

....

1. Sulphur; 2. 18; 3. Lady Godiva; 4. Red; 5. Topiary; 6. Tomato;
7. Twilight of the Gods; 8. Blackcurrant; 9. San Andreas;
10. Knitting stitches; 11. Felix; 12. Yahoo

....

NUMBER 3

....

1. Lily; 2. England; 3. Half sister; 4. Bank of England; 5. None;
6. Howard Hughes; 7. St Mungo; 8. Champion; 9. 1200;
10. Václav Havel (Czechoslovakia); 11. Pegasus;
12. Johnny Dankworth

....

NUMBER 4

....

1. Comma; 2. Tashkent; 3. 28; 4. Delft; 5. Caspar, Balthasar, Melchior;
6. Lee; 7. Ayr; 8. Cricket; 9. York; 10. Bell-ringing; 11. Gregorian;
12. Divine wind

....

ANSWERS
GENERAL KNOWLEDGE

. . . .

NUMBER 5

. . . .

1. Jenny Shipley; 2. K; 3. Abigail; 4. Sign language; 5. Edward VII;
6. Chinese Mandarin; 7. Comedy Store; 8. Beau; 9. Doncaster;
10. Isambard Kingdom Brunel; 11. "The People's Car";
12. Conquest, War, Famine, Death

NUMBER 6

. . . .

1. 27; 2. Stalagmites; 3. North Atlantic; 4. Malcolm Maclaren;
5. Spanish Riding School; 6. Infallible; 7. Knot; 8. 1960;
9. Alec Issigonis; 10. Boat; 11. 26; 12. John Galsworthy

NUMBER 7

. . . .

1. Very Superior Old Pale; 2. Jackie Milburn; 3. Twiggy; 4. Black;
5. Mob; 6. Benjamin Franklin; 7. France and New Zealand;
8. Peter Tchaikovsky; 9. Bad Homburg (homburg hat);
10. Simon and Garfunkel; 11. H; 12. Ten

NUMBER 8

. . . .

1. Chemistry, Economics, Literature, Medicine, Peace, Physics;
2. Their letters are in alphabetical order; 3. Gibbs SR toothpaste;
4. Statue of Zeus; 5. Vincent van Gogh; 6. Hendrik Verwoerd;
7. Giant Panda; 8. Nikolai Gogol; 9. Fibre-optic Link Around the Globe;
10. Kukri; 11. Bobby Darin; 12. St Fiacre

ANSWERS
GENERAL KNOWLEDGE

. . . .

NUMBER 9

. . . .

1. "Angel of Death"; 2. Ron Greenwood; 3. Tanzania; 4. Banknotes;
5. Captain James Cook; 6. Sparky; 7. Hats; 8. Speedway racing;
9. Adam and the Ants; 10. Donald Duck's nephews; 11. Wednesday;
12. Both

NUMBER 10

. . . .

1. Eton College; 2. Four; 3. W J Burley; 4. Apple; 5. Japan; 6. Horse;
7. Peter Parker; 8. France's; 9. Model T Ford car; 10. N;
11. Study of words; 12. Yom Kippur

NUMBER 11

. . . .

1. 150; 2. Dogger; 3. Buddha; 4. Drunk; 5. Tennessee;
6. Richard Burton; 7. York; 8. Gloucestershire and Nottinghamshire;
9. Andorra, Belgium, Germany, Italy, Luxembourg, Monaco, Spain,
Switzerland; 10. Bolero; 11. Four; 12. Belgium

NUMBER 12

. . . .

1. Phineas T Barnum; 2. Donkey; 3. The Pope; 4. Karl Marx and
Friedrich Engels; 5. Bournemouth; 6. Greenwich; 7. Ennio Morricone;
8. Anaheim; 9. Toad; 10. Belshazzar; 11. Fatted goose liver;
12. Obituaries

ANSWERS
GENERAL KNOWLEDGE

NUMBER 13

1. Imitation gold; 2. Napoleon Bonaparte; 3. Elephant; 4. Plane crash; 5. The ear; 6. One-sixth; 7. Zadie Smith; 8. Ann Jones; 9. Potato; 10. Benjamin Britten; 11. David; 12. Marilyn Monroe

NUMBER 14

1. Aardvark; 2. Petrograd and Leningrad; 3. Two hours; 4. Scilly Isles; 5. Nazi Party; 6. Mumbai; 7. Quotient; 8. Peter Bonetti; 9. Omega; 10. Roy Hattersley; 11. Fifth; 12. Trampolining

NUMBER 15

1. The Gambia; 2. *The Hunchback of Notre Dame*; 3. Munich; 4. "Thou Shalt Not Kill"; 5. Four; 6. Fractions; 7. "Boy"; 8. Bayonne; 9. Charles Tingwell; 10. Les Invalides; 11. Phyllis Dorothy; 12. La Bourse

NUMBER 16

1. Yeovil Town; 2. *Midnight's Children;* 3. Lambeth; 4. The Taoiseach; 5. Nimbus; 6. Nyree Dawn Porter; 7. Orange; 8. Greta Louisa Gustafsson; 9. Cresta Run; 10. Thomas Kyd; 11. 70mph; 12. Flower arranging

ANSWERS
GENERAL KNOWLEDGE

NUMBER 17

1. Arizona; 2. BBC's; 3. Lentils; 4. Nicholas Blake; 5. Phidias;
6. Randy "The Ram" Robinson; 7. Willie John McBride; 8. Bolsover;
9. Shell; 10. Ben Elton; 11. Three; 12. Lower Loxley Hall

NUMBER 18

1. The Brontës; 2. Sir Alec Douglas-Home; 3. John and Hayley Mills;
4. *Ich dien;* 5. Jezebel; 6. John Milton; 7. Surfing; 8. 12;
9. Erich Maria Remarque; 10. Hanoi; 11. Stephen Frears;
12. In a church

NUMBER 19

1. *Aquae Sulis*; 2. Top hat; 3. Bobby Charlton; 4. Westminster Abbey;
5. Miller; 6. Washington Irving; 7. Three Musketeers;
8. Cricket and hockey; 9. Bing Crosby; 10. *Gypsy Moth;* 11. Nipper;
12. William Wordsworth

NUMBER 20

1. Danny Kaye; 2. Chantilly; 3. The Blue Peter; 4. Nucleus; 5. 1919;
6. March; 7. Right; 8. Glyndebourne; 9. 336; 10. The house;
11. Doris Lessing; 12. Marvin Hamlisch

ANSWERS
GENERAL KNOWLEDGE

NUMBER 21

1. *1984*; 2. Battle of the Bulge; 3. Margot Fonteyn; 4. Scampi;
5. Hawser; 6. Hermit crab; 7. The Three Graces; 8. St Mark;
9. Graham Taylor; 10. Ali G; 11. Dan Quayle; 12. Sir Humphrey Davy

NUMBER 22

1. RAF's; 2. Schultz; 3. Ra; 4. Carisbrooke Castle; 5. Bahrain;
6. Allen Ginsberg; 7. Eric Coates; 8. Yellow; 9. Huw Weldon;
10. Damascus; 11. Fish; 12. *Bleak House*

NUMBER 23

1. Christian Science; 2. Butt; 3. Sloane Ranger; 4. Tides;
5. Sir William Walton; 6. Raven; 7. Elton John; 8. January 1st;
9. Edward Gibbon; 10. Knights Templar; 11. Fishing flies; 12. 1981

NUMBER 24

1. Climbing plant; 2. Revelation; 3. Tony Benn; 4. Cubism;
5. Ivy League; 6. 7/10th; 7. Tony Hancock's; 8. Geoffrey Rush;
9. Morris Garages; 10. Judo (belt); 11. T S Eliot's; 12. Twice cooked